Experiments
with Heat

Books by Harry Sootin

Experiments in Magnetism and Electricity
Isaac Newton
Gregor Mendel: Father of Science and Genetics
Michael Faraday: From Errand Boy to Master Physicist
Robert Boyle: Founder of Modern Chemistry
Twelve Pioneers of Science
Experiments with Machines and Matter
Light Experiments, for Home Workshop and School Laboratory
Science Experiments with Sound

Experiments with Heat

by Harry Sootin

illustrated by Frank Aloise

New York

W · W · Norton & Company · Inc ·

Contents U. S. 1249881

Foreword

As in the other books of this series, the emphasis in *Experiments with Heat* is on hands and brains, on doing and thinking. The materials used in the experiments are inexpensive, readily available, and easily put together. The stress throughout is on *understanding* rather than on the construction of complicated devices or gadgets.

Every science student can profit from laboratory experiences. He must be allowed to arrange simple apparatus, to improvise, adjust, fumble, and puzzle over why things "happen." This, of course, cannot be done in a hurry. The experiments here, for example, might best be done at home during long leisurely afternoons or evenings.

In recent years so much new subject matter has been added to science courses that there is simply no time for the student to "try" things by himself and at his own pace. This is unfortunate, for teachers know that the *laboratory approach to science* is far superior to any other. It can not — and should not — be replaced by lectures, films, television or classroom demonstrations.

To get the most out of *Experiments with Heat,* the student should regard the experiments and explanations as *beginnings.* A more thorough understanding of many important scientific principles awaits those who make intelligent use of the reading list near the end of the book. It is hoped that the suggestions on page 90 will help guide inquiring minds to an understanding in depth of some, if not all, of the subjects treated.

facts and ideas about . . .

Expansion of Solids

You are going to move a match or candle flame along the length of a copper wire to find out if its length changes with changes in temperature.

The kinetic theory of matter: All matter — whether solid or liquid or gas — is composed of tiny particles called molecules. These particles are in a state of continual motion. In gases the molecules move about at extremely high speeds. In liquids the molecules are closer together and move less freely than in gases. In solids, where the molecules are relatively close to one another, the motion consists of vibrations about fixed points.

According to the kinetic theory, adding heat to a substance increases the motion of its molecules. Correspondingly, subtracting heat from a substance, or cooling it, diminishes the motion of its molecules. Does this explain the changes in length of the copper wire in your experiment? Why?

Some solids expand more than others when subjected to *equal* changes in temperature. A piece of copper wire one foot long will expand seventeen-millionths (0.000017) of a foot when its temperature is raised one degree centigrade. The corresponding increase for steel is twelve-millionths (0.000012) of a foot; for aluminum twenty-three millionths (0.000023) of a foot.

The numbers or fractions noted above are called *coefficients* of *linear expansion*. The coefficient of linear expansion of a solid is the amount that each *unit of length* expands for one degree rise in temperature. Most linear expansion tables are in terms of *per degree centigrade*. See page 25 on how to change temperature readings from Fahrenheit to centigrade.

Telephone wires strung on poles sag noticeably in hot weather. Why? When railroad tracks are laid, spaces are left between their ends. Why? The sections of a concrete highway are separated from each other by narrow spaces filled with asphalt or tar. Why?

SOME INTERESTING FACTS ABOUT THE EXPANSION OF SOLIDS:

(a) Your heated copper wire will expand not only in length but in all directions *at the same rate*. The wire becomes longer and wider at the same time.

(b) A mile of railroad track may be as much as a yard longer in summer than in winter. A thousand-foot steel bridge may change in length by several inches during the year. Why?

(c) A special low-expansion glass like Pyrex (0.000003) expands about one-third as much as ordinary glass (0.000009). Why are Pyrex utensils often used for cooking and baking?

(d) Certain metal alloys have extremely low expansion coefficients. Invar steel, a nickel-iron alloy, for example, has an expansion coefficient of 0.0000009. It is used for surveyor's tapes, clock pendulums, and standard meters. Can you explain why?

Try pouring boiling water into a thick glass container. The vessel will usually crack or break. Which gets hotter first — the inside or the outside of the glass vessel? Is glass a good conductor of heat? The glass breaks because of *differential expansion:* that is, the inside expands faster than the outside.

Here is a list of expansion coefficients of some common materials:

COEFFICIENTS OF LINEAR EXPANSION (CENTIGRADE)

aluminum	0.000023	Invar	0.0000009
brass	0.000018	(0.3 nickel)	
silver	0.000019		
copper	0.000017	quartz	0.0000005
nickel	0.000013	glass (common)	0.000009
steel	0.000012	glass (Pyrex)	0.000003
iron (cast)	0.000011	concrete	0.000012
zinc	0.000026		

Expansion of Solids When Heated

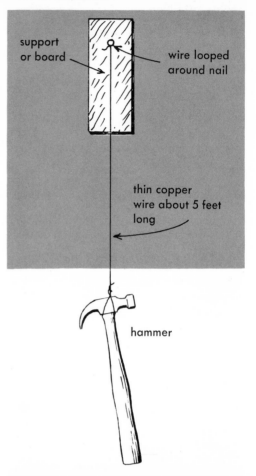

support or board

wire looped around nail

thin copper wire about 5 feet long

hammer

A

DO THIS: Attach one end of wire to a nail in a board. Let wire be stretched taut by tying a hammer or wrench to other end. Use bell wire, or better, #20 or #22 copper wire. The thinner the wire the less likely to "kink."

B

Attach matchstick or toothpick to end of ruler. Use glue or rubber band. The matchstick or toothpick will serve as a pointer.

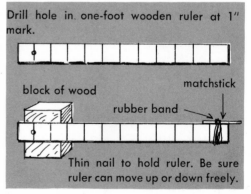

Drill hole in one-foot wooden ruler at 1" mark.

block of wood

matchstick

rubber band

Thin nail to hold ruler. Be sure ruler can move up or down freely.

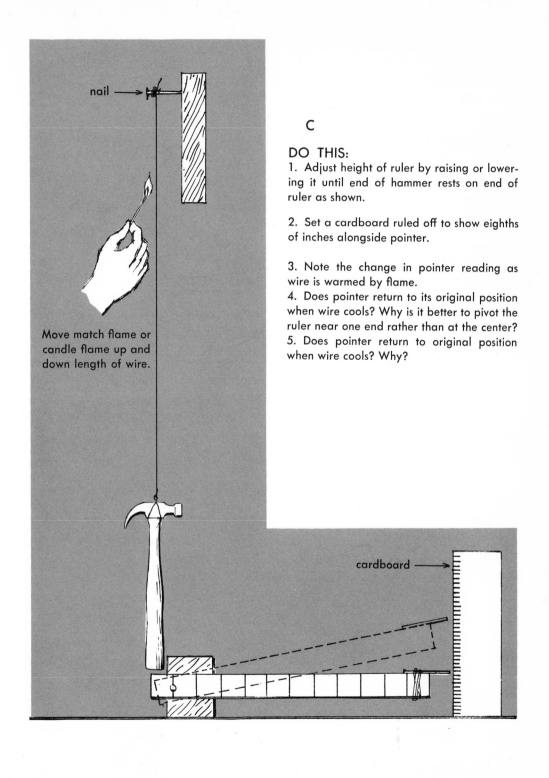

nail →

Move match flame or candle flame up and down length of wire.

C

DO THIS:

1. Adjust height of ruler by raising or lowering it until end of hammer rests on end of ruler as shown.

2. Set a cardboard ruled off to show eighths of inches alongside pointer.

3. Note the change in pointer reading as wire is warmed by flame.

4. Does pointer return to its original position when wire cools? Why is it better to pivot the ruler near one end rather than at the center?

5. Does pointer return to original position when wire cools? Why?

cardboard →

The Stretching of Rubber

You are going to draw out a rubber band suddenly while the edges of your lips are in slight contact with the middle of the band. Does the rubber band become warmer or cooler on being stretched? Try it.

After stretching the rubber band you will hold it in its elongated position for a few minutes so that it may return to room temperature. You will then let it go back to its normal length suddenly while holding your lips to the middle as before. Does the rubber band become warmer or cooler on contracting? Try it.

The above phenomenon was first described in 1858 by J. Gough, an English scientist. It was regarded as extraordinary because bars or wires of other materials all behaved in an opposite manner. For example, a piece of metal, when suddenly expanded, becomes cool — not warm. A spiral spring, for example, will become lower in temperature when suddenly pulled out, and higher in temperature when suddenly allowed to draw in.

Gough immediately went on to show that a stretched rubber band with a weight hanging on one end would contract when heated with a force sufficient to raise the weight. You will try a similar experiment, using a few books tied to the lower end of a rubber band as the stretching weight. Will your rubber band, on being heated, contract and pull the weight up? Try it. Will your stretched rubber band return to original length on cooling? Try it. Follow the simple directions on the experiment page.

The earlier explanation of this phenomenon was rather simple: When rubber is heated it contracts. When pulled out, it assumes dimensions it would normally have at a lower temperature. The result is that inter-molecular energy is set free and the rubber becomes warm.

But according to the kinetic theory of matter (see page 8) expansion in volume as the result of heating is due to the increased molecular activity: their more rapid movement or vibrations cause the molecules to move farther apart. Why should rubber behave differently?

The modern explanation is much more complicated. Rubber consists of long-chain molecules in a state of tangled disorder. The internal disorganization of the rubber molecules resembles that of a gas rather than a solid. The rubber molecules are in constant random disorder. Stretching the rubber by means of a weight tied to one end interferes with the random motion of the rubber molecules. The stretching introduces a certain amount of alignment or order in the molecular motion.

Suppose you proceed to heat the rubber while it is in the stretched or aligned state. The external heat causes an increase in the random motion of the molecules. The molecules begin to move with greater energy and in an even more disorderly fashion, thus overcoming the alignment produced by the stretching. The result is that the rubber band exerts increased tension and contracts. Cartilage, skin, leather, and many plastics behave like rubber in that they contract when heated.

Try to find out more about the interesting concepts that are involved in the explanation of the contraction of rubber when heated: Brownian movement, entropy or the state of random disorder, and the second law of thermodynamics. (See p. 90 for reading list.)

The Stretching of Rubber

1/4″

rubber band after cutting
and opening to full length

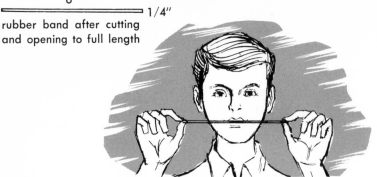

1. Place lips lightly at middle of rubber strip
and *quickly* stretch rubber to about 3 to 4
times its original length.

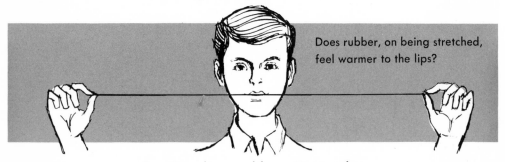

Does rubber, on being stretched,
feel warmer to the lips?

2. Now keep rubber strip in above
stretched position for 3 to 5 minutes.
This will allow rubber to return to
room temperature.

Quickly release rubber so
that it returns to its original
length.

Does rubber now feel
cooler to your lips?

Try the above experiments with the rubber
band several times.

3. Stretching and temperature.

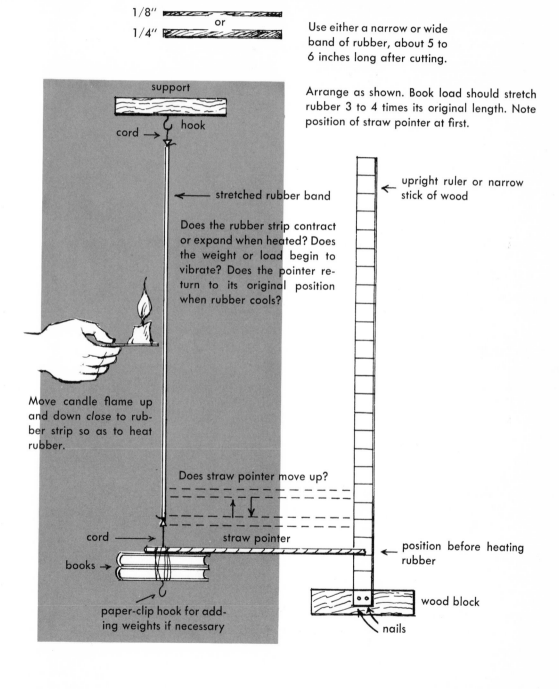

1/8"

or

1/4"

Use either a narrow or wide band of rubber, about 5 to 6 inches long after cutting.

support

cord → hook

Arrange as shown. Book load should stretch rubber 3 to 4 times its original length. Note position of straw pointer at first.

← stretched rubber band

Does the rubber strip contract or expand when heated? Does the weight or load begin to vibrate? Does the pointer return to its original position when rubber cools?

← upright ruler or narrow stick of wood

Move candle flame up and down *close* to rubber strip so as to heat rubber.

Does straw pointer move up?

cord →

straw pointer

books →

← position before heating rubber

paper-clip hook for adding weights if necessary

wood block

nails

The Bimetallic Strip

You are going to attach a strip of brass to a strip of zinc by bending back flaps cut into each, as described on the experiment page. You will then have a bimetallic strip, sometimes called a compound bar.

The two attached strips will be of the same length and cross section. The expansion coefficient (see page 8) of brass is 0.000018 and that of zinc is 0.000026. Which will expand more when your bimetallic strip is held over a flame? Why?

Since the two strips are attached to each other, the zinc with the higher expansion coefficient cannot become longer by simply sliding past the brass. Can you explain the warping or bending that occurs when a bimetallic strip is heated? Which metal will always be on the outside of the bend or curve? Why? We say that such warping is caused by differential expansion. Can you explain this statement?

Will your bimetallic strip straighten out again on cooling? Suppose you cool it still further by placing the straight bimetallic strip in a refrigerator. Will it curve or bend? Which metal will be on the outside of the bend now? Why? Try it.

The use of brass and zinc for your experiment was suggested only because these metals can be purchased, in hardware stores in the form of small rolls of linoleum bindings. Actually the metals most often used in industrial bimetallic strips are brass (0.000018) and invar steel. (0.0000009).

Invar steel is an alloy containing 30% nickel. Its expansion coefficient, as noted above, is extremely low. How many times greater is the expansion coefficient of brass than that of invar steel — two times, 20 times, or 200 times? Suppose you start with a straight bimetallic strip of brass-invar steel. Which metal will be found on the outside of the bend when this bimetallic strip is heated? Why?

Bimetallic strips are used in the metallic thermometers that indicate the temperatures of ovens. Bimetallic strips are utilized in the thermostats that control the temperatures of house-heating systems, electric irons, and refrigerators. Bimetallic strips are also used in making balance wheels for fine watches.

You will also try to compare the expansion rates of copper and iron, using wires of these materials of the same length and diameter. When the copper and iron wires are heated by the method described in the experiment, which will sag more? Why? If you can get aluminum wire of the same diameter as the other wires, try the experiment using all three.

You will form a circle of aluminum wire around a glass marble. Tighten the aluminum wire circle slightly so that the marble will not slip through the loop. Try warming the aluminum circle in the flame. Will the cold marble slip through now? Why? Also try heating the aluminum circle while the marble is resting inside it. Explain what happens. Note that the expansion coefficient of aluminum is 0.000023 while that of ordinary glass is 0.000009.

The Bimetallic Strip

1.

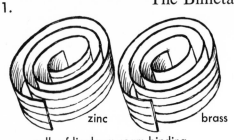

zinc   brass

rolls of linoleum seam binding
9/16" wide

Buy a small roll of zinc binding and another of brass binding at any hardware store.

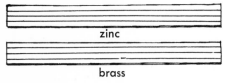

zinc

brass

Cut off equal lengths of each, about 15 inches. Straighten by smoothing with fingers.

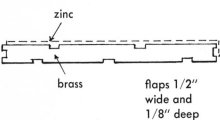

zinc

brass   flaps 1/2"
wide and
1/8" deep

With pair of snips make slits as shown. Now bend flaps under or over, tightening with pliers to lock them together securely. The more flaps the better.

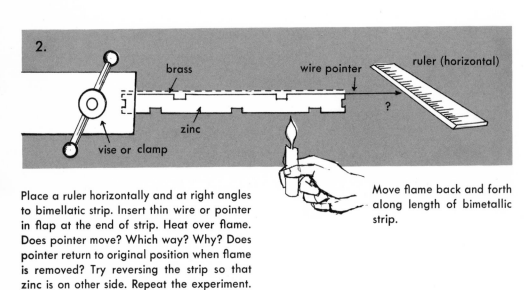

ruler (horizontal)

brass   wire pointer

zinc

vise or clamp

Place a ruler horizontally and at right angles to bimellatic strip. Insert thin wire or pointer in flap at the end of strip. Heat over flame. Does pointer move? Which way? Why? Does pointer return to original position when flame is removed? Try reversing the strip so that zinc is on other side. Repeat the experiment.

Move flame back and forth along length of bimetallic strip.

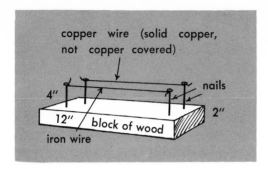

copper wire (solid copper, not copper covered)

nails

4"

12" block of wood

2"

iron wire

3. Unequal expansion of brass and iron.

Hammer long nails into block of wood as shown. Make distances between each pair *equal*. Make wires taut. Use #16 or #18 wire. Copper and iron wire should be of same diameter. Buy *iron* wire and *solid* copper wire at hardware store.

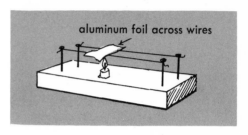

aluminum foil across wires

Place candle flame under middle of aluminum foil. Heat is conducted from *center* of foil to the wires.

Wires are both taut before heating.

Which wire sags noticeably on being heated? Why? Do the wires become taut and parallel again on cooling?

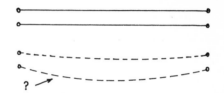

?

4. Try this.

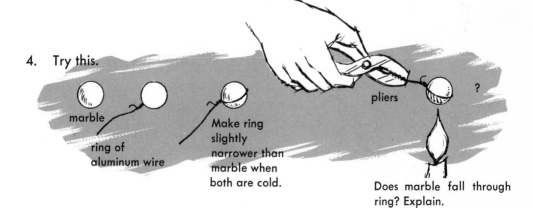

marble

ring of aluminum wire

Make ring slightly narrower than marble when both are cold.

pliers

?

Does marble fall through ring? Explain.

Also try heating only the wire loop. Will the cold marble drop through hot loop?

facts and ideas about . . .

Thermostats

You are going to pry open a small, inexpensive oven thermometer and remove its coiled bimetallic strip. These small coils are usually composed of brass and invar steel. Before taking the coil out study the construction of the metallic thermometer. How do changes in temperature cause the needle to move?

Can you tell which side of the bimetallic strip is brass and which is invar steel? Try rubbing a small section with fine sandpaper to reveal the color of the brass. Or pull the end of the coil out and then warm this end in a match flame. If the end section is curved to begin with and the curve straightens out on being heated, then the metal on the *inside* of the curve must be brass (0.000018) rather than invar steel (0.0000009). Can you explain why?

You will then attach the bimetallic strip to a board and arrange a wire pointer and ruler as described on the experiment page. Will your bimetallic strip respond to warm breath? to the presence of a jar of ice water? Try it.

A thermostat is a device used for controlling temperatures in rooms, fish pools, electric irons, electric refrigerators, and so forth. The word thermostat comes from the Greek *thermē*, meaning heat, and *statikos*, to make stand. In general, thermostats utilize the expansion of a solid or liquid or gas to close or open electrical switches, close or open dampers, or regulate a supply of fuel.

The thermostat in your home or classroom keeps the air temperature from falling too low or rising too high. The thermostat operates by means of a bimetallic strip, the end of which moves to one side when the air is too cool and the other side when the air is too warm.

Suppose the room cools beyond a certain set temperature. The movement of the bimetallic strip to one side results in its touching an electrical contact — i.e., it closes a switch or completes an electrical circuit. The closing of the switch starts the motor of the oil burner in the basement. As the radiators become warm the temperature of the room rises. Soon the heat of the room causes the bimetallic strip to move away from the contact point. The circuit is broken. The motor in the oil burner stops running. What happens when the room cools down again?

You are going to arrange a simple thermostat circuit using the bimetallic strip extracted from the oven thermometer. Follow the simple directions. Can you get the bulb to light when the end of the strip is warmed in a flame? Try it. How would you arrange the circuit so as to make the bulb light when the strip is cooled rather than heated? Try it.

A thermostat does not necessarily have to open or close electric switches. In the automobile radiator, for example, there is a thermostat that slows down the flow of water to the radiator while the engine is cold. As soon as the engine gets hot, the water in the jacket around it gets hot, too. This hot water causes the bimetallic coiled spring in the thermostat to push open the valve that allows water to flow through the radiator freely. This type of thermostat works mechanically. The bimetallic spring is sturdy enough to open and close a valve.

Thermostat

1.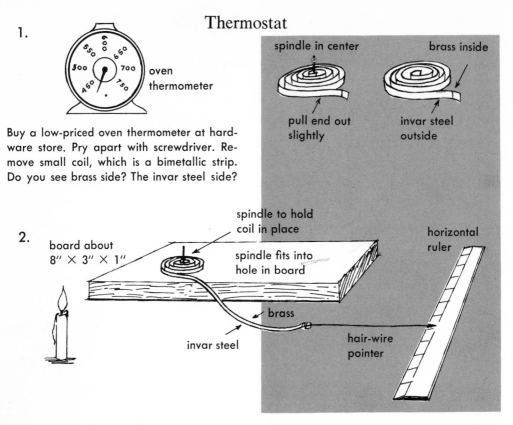

oven thermometer

Buy a low-priced oven thermometer at hardware store. Pry apart with screwdriver. Remove small coil, which is a bimetallic strip. Do you see brass side? The invar steel side?

spindle in center

brass inside

pull end out slightly

invar steel outside

2.

board about 8″ × 3″ × 1″

spindle to hold coil in place

spindle fits into hole in board

horizontal ruler

brass

invar steel

hair-wire pointer

Make small nail hole in board. Insert spindle. Pull about 3 inches of bimetallic strip out from coil as shown. Attach very fine wire, called hair wire and available at hardware stores, to end of strip. Place ruler in position to show movement of pointer. Try *warming* the pulled-out part of strip with a flame. Does pointer move inward or outward? Why? Does it return to original position when flame is removed? Explain.

3. How sensitive is your bimetallic strip? Try the following.

Blow breath against strip.

Bring jar or pan of hot water close to strip.

Bring jar or pan of ice water close to strip.

4. Arrange a thermostat circuit. You will need these materials, all available at hardware stores.

No. 6 dry cell

miniature porcelain socket with a 1-1/2 volt bulb

strip of bell wire or ordinary lamp cord

Use board with bimetallic strip from previous experiment. Make connections to dry cell and bulb as indicated.

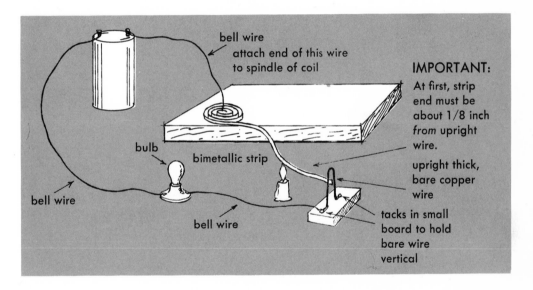

bell wire attach end of this wire to spindle of coil

IMPORTANT: At first, strip end must be about 1/8 inch *from* upright wire.

upright thick, bare copper wire

bulb

bimetallic strip

bell wire

bell wire

tacks in small board to hold bare wire vertical

DO THIS: When cold, the bimetallic strip end is close to, but *not* touching, upright bare copper wire. Now bring flame near bimetallic strip. Does heat make it curve outward and *touch* bare upright wire? Does bulb then light up? Why? Take flame away. Does bulb soon go out again? Why? Repeat. Try changing width of gap between bare wire and bimetallic strip if bulb does not light up quickly.

facts and ideas about . . .

Expansion of Gases

You are going to cool a narrow cylinder of air in order to find out how gases respond to changes in temperatures.

The air column you will use will be inside an ordinary drinking straw. A drop of water within the straw will act as a movable piston. In other words, this drop of water will not only lock in the air beneath it but also exert a constant pressure.

In 1802 a French chemist, Gay-Lussac, discovered that all gases have the same *volume coefficient of expansion*, namely, $\frac{1}{273}$ or expressed decimally, 0.00366.

This means that the volume of every gas will increase $\frac{1}{273}$ of its volume at 0° centigrade for every degree rise in temperature (centigrade), provided the pressure is kept constant or unchanged.

For example, suppose a gas like air occupies 100 cubic centimeters at 0° C. What will be the increase in volume of this gas when its temperature is raised to 20° C?

The gas will expand $\frac{1}{273}$ of its volume at 0° C for each degree rise in temperature. For a 20-degree rise the volume will increase 20 times $\frac{1}{273}$ or $\frac{20}{273}$ of the original volume. Multiplying this fraction by the original 100 cubic centimeters gives 7.3 cubic centimeters for the *increase* in volume.

Suppose your cylinder of air were closed at *both* ends. Will the volume of air in the straw change when its temperature is raised? Will the pressure of the air inside the straw change? Explain. Try it.

24

Why will a gas expand when heated and contract when cooled? According to the kinetic theory, temperature is a measure of the average energy of the molecules of a substance. An increase in temperature means an increase in the average molecular energy. The result, when the piston is movable, is an increase in the space or volume occupied by the molecules of the gas. Why?

You should know how to change from centigrade to Fahrenheit, since Gay-Lussac's law is true only for the centigrade scale. Two simple formulas are used for converting temperatures.

To change from centigrade to Fahrenheit temperatures do the following: Multiply by $\frac{9}{5}$ and add 32, or $°F = \frac{9}{5} C + 32$

Example: hange 20° C to Fahrenheit
$$°F = \frac{9}{5} (20) + 32$$
$$°F = 36 + 32 = 68 \qquad \text{Ans. } 68° F$$

To change from Fahrenheit to centigrade do the following: Subtract 32° and then multiply by $\frac{5}{9}$; or $°C = \frac{5}{9} (F - 32)$

Example: Change 86° F to centigrade
$$°C = \frac{5}{9} (F - 32)$$
$$°C = \frac{5}{9} (86 - 32)$$
$$°C = \frac{5}{9} (54)$$
$$°C = 30 \qquad \text{Ans. } 30° C$$

The Expansion of Gases When Heated

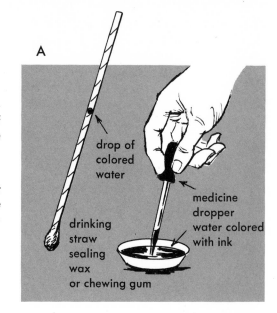

A

drop of colored water

drinking straw

sealing wax

or chewing gum

medicine dropper

water colored with ink

DO THIS: Take drinking "straw" of a natural color and made of plastic material if possible. Seal end in hot sealing wax or use chewing gum.

Add a drop of colored water to straw. Get it about halfway down by means of medicine dropper. Try tapping or poking with toothpick.

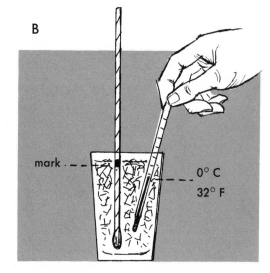

B

mark

0° C
32° F

Set the straw in tall glass containing crushed ice and water. Stir with thermometer. After 3 minutes mark place to which drop has descended as a result of the contraction of the air.

Now you know what volume or space the air under the drop occupies at 0° C or 32° F.

Mark position of drop on straw while it is in an ice and water mixture.

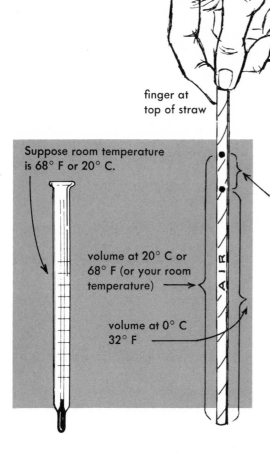

finger at
top of straw

Suppose room temperature
is 68° F or 20° C.

volume at 20° C or
68° F (or your room
temperature) →

volume at 0° C
32° F

C   Take straw out of ice water. Hold it in the air for 5 minutes. Does drop move up the straw? Why? Find temperature of the air in the room.

Measure the change in volume with a ruler.

Measure the following in centimeters:
1. The length of the column of air under drop at 0° C or 32° F.

2. The length of the column of air under the drop at room temperature.

Now subtract to find out the increase in length of this column of air.

D   In the case illustrated above the increase should be $\dfrac{20}{273}$ of the original column at 0° C.

When heated, gases expand $\dfrac{1}{273}$ of their volume at 0° C for every degree rise in temperature (centigrade). Try it. See how close you get to the correct figure.

NOTE: See previous page for changing Fahrenheit to centigrade.

Temperature and Heat Content

You are going to place a steel marble and a glass marble, both of the same size, in boiling water for five minutes. At the end of that time both marbles will be at the temperature of the boiling water, namely 100° C (212° F). Why?

The temperature of the steel ball is exactly the same as the temperature of the glass marble. Does this mean that the quantity of heat in both marbles is equal too?

You will answer this question by taking the hot marbles out of the boiling water and quickly placing them on a cake of paraffin wax. Heat will flow from the hot spheres of steel and glass to the cold paraffin. Why? Some paraffin will melt. The marble that contains the greater quantity of heat in it will sink deeper into the paraffin. Which will it be — the steel or the glass? Try it.

The observation that different materials, though of the same size and temperature, contain different quantities of heat was first made by Joseph Black (1728-1799), a Scottish scientist.

Suppose you find that the steel ball gives up more heat than the glass marble on cooling from 100° C to the temperature of the melting wax. Therefore the heat content of the steel ball must have been greater than that of the glass marble. Another way of saying this is that a steel ball has greater heat capacity than a glass marble of the same size.

Keep in mind that temperature is not the same as quantity of heat. Temperature is a measure of the hotness or coldness of a substance. Temperature tells us about the average energy of motion of the particles of a substance. A cup of boiling water and a gallon of boiling water will each cause a thermometer to rise to 100° C. Which required more fuel or heat to raise it to this temperature? Why?

Heat, according to the kinetic theory, is the total amount of the kinetic energy of the particles. How much heat a marble or frying pan or pot of water contains depends not only on its temperature but also on its mass and the kind of material each is made of. In your experiment with the steel and glass marbles only the temperatures are the same: the weights of the marbles are unequal and they are made of different materials.

Temperature is measured in degrees. How is heat measured? Water is used as the standard substance. The quantity of heat required to raise the temperature of one gram of water one centigrade degree is called a *calorie*. The quantity of heat required to raise the temperature of one pound of water one Fahrenheit degree is called a British thermal unit (Btu).

The term *heat capacity* means the quantity of heat that a body or substance requires for one degree rise in temperature. Note that the number of calories required to raise the temperature of a body one degree is the same as the number of calories given up when the temperature of the same body falls one degree.

You will also try raising the temperature of screws of similar size but different materials to 100° C and then placing them on paraffin wax as before. Will the heat capacities of the brass, steel, and aluminum screws be different? Try it. Can you explain your results?

Temperature and Heat Content

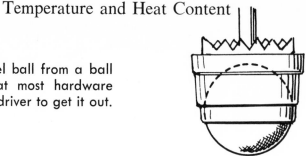

1. Extract the steel ball from a ball caster, available at most hardware stores. Use a screwdriver to get it out.

get a glass marble of same size as the steel ball.

steel ball   glass marble

2. Heat content.

Place steel ball and glass marble in pan of water. Boil water for 5 minutes to bring temperature of ball and marble up to 100° C (212° F).

cake of paraffin wax such as is used for canning fruits, etc. Buy it at ten-cent or hardware stores.

paraffin wax

Now take steel ball and marble out of the boiling water, wipe dry, and quickly place them on the cake of paraffin.

Examine after 5 minutes.

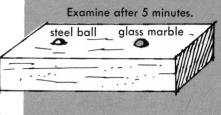

steel ball   glass marble

Both were at the same temperature. Which melted more paraffin and therefore sank deeper — the steel ball or the glass marble? What *contained* more *heat*? Explain.

3. Heat content: comparing steel, brass, and aluminum

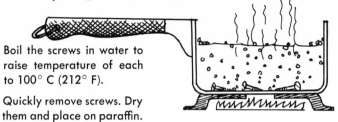

Boil the screws in water to raise temperature of each to 100° C (212° F).

Quickly remove screws. Dry them and place on paraffin.

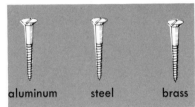

aluminum   steel   brass

Use large screws.

The three screws must be of the same size.

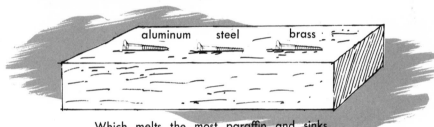

aluminum   steel   brass

Which melts the most paraffin and sinks deepest? Which melts the least paraffin and sinks least? Which contained the most heat? Explain.

4. Try this additional experiment:

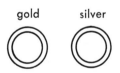

gold   silver

If you have a gold and a silver ring of same size and thickness, try them.

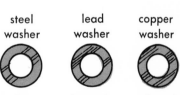

steel   lead   copper
washer   washer   washer

Use large, heavy washers of same diameter and thickness.

DO THIS: Place in boiling water for 5 minutes, then dry and place each on the paraffin. Which washer has the highest heat content? The lowest?

facts and ideas about . . .

Specific Heat

Using a homemade balance, you will weigh out a piece of aluminum foil equal to the weight of a silver coin. You will crumple up the aluminum foil into a compact cylinder and then heat it and the silver coin in boiling water as in the previous experiment. The hot silver and aluminum will then be placed on a cake of paraffin. You will estimate the quantity of heat contained in each metal by the amount of wax melted.

How does this experiment differ from the one you did before? This time you are using the same mass — i.e., *same number* of grams of each metal. Keep in mind that heat capacity depends not only on the material but the mass of a body. In this experiment, by using the same number of grams of each material, you will be able to compare the heat capacities of two materials, aluminum and silver. Think about this.

When we deal with a unit mass like a gram or a pound of a substance then we are in a position to speak of the *specific heat* of that substance. The number of calories required to raise the temperature of one gram of a substance 1° centigrade is called the specific heat of that substance. Each material has its own specific heat. Aluminum, for example, is listed in tables as having a specific heat of 0.21. This simply means that about one-fifth of a calorie is required to raise the temperature of one gram of aluminum through 1° C.

How about water? What is its specific heat? Think of the definition of a calorie: the quantity of heat required to raise the temperature of one gram of water through 1° C. Therefore the specific heat of water, by definition, is 1. Do you see why?

Here is a short list of specific heats:

	(In calories per gram per degree centigrade)		
aluminum	0.21	water (by definition)	1.00
brass	0.09	ethyl alcohol	0.60
copper	0.093		
glass	0.16	paraffin wax	0.7
iron	0.11		
lead	0.03		
silver	0.056		

Notice that the lighter metals require more heat, or more calories, than the heavier metals for a one-degree rise in temperature per gram of metal. Is there any explanation for this? In general, the lighter the atoms of which a substance is composed the more numerous must be the *number* of atoms in a gram or pound of it. Why? Therefore more heat must be added to the lighter substance to produce a given rise in temperature.

The specific heat of all common solids and liquids is much less than that of water. For example, mineral oil has a specific heat of 0.5 and ethyl alcohol 0.60. Suppose you had to select a liquid for the water jacket surrounding the engine of an automobile. Under *normal* conditions, which liquid — water, ethyl alcohol, or mineral oil — will absorb more heat from the engine for every degree rise in temperature? Which will cool the engine more efficiently? Why?

The moderating effect on climate of large bodies of water is partly due to the high specific heat of water. The oceans, for example, store up a vast amount of heat during the summer. What does the specific heat of water have to do with this process? In winter, the land mass quickly loses the heat it had accumulated during the summer. Why? In winter, therefore, the oceans become warmer than the land. Does this explain why coastal regions in general have warmer winters and cooler summers than nearby inland regions? Why?

Specific Heat

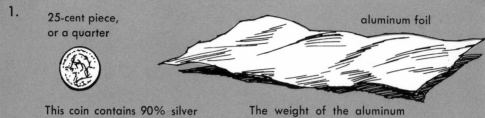

1.

25-cent piece, or a quarter

aluminum foil

This coin contains 90% silver and 10% copper, but regard it as all silver in this experiment.

The weight of the aluminum foil should be exactly equal to the weight of the 25-cent piece.

2. If you have a small scale, such as is used for weighing letters, weigh the 25-cent coin and then get an equal weight of aluminum foil. If not, make your own beam balance as follows:

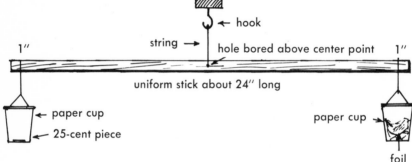

hook

string →

hole bored above center point

1″

1″

uniform stick about 24″ long

paper cup

25-cent piece

paper cup

foil

Suspend stick as shown above. If the stick is not quite horizontal, add bits of paper to higher paper cup. Now add 25-cent piece to one cup and add strips of aluminum foil to the other cup until they balance.

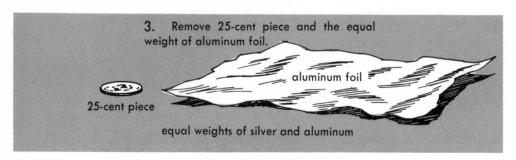

3. Remove 25-cent piece and the equal weight of aluminum foil.

aluminum foil

25-cent piece

equal weights of silver and aluminum

4.

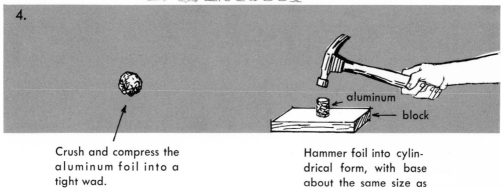

Crush and compress the aluminum foil into a tight wad.

Hammer foil into cylindrical form, with base about the same size as the 25-cent coin.

5.

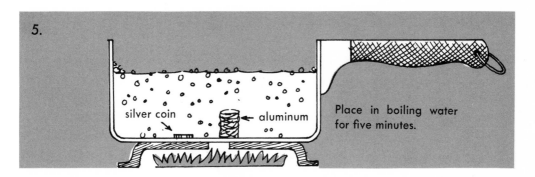

Place in boiling water for five minutes.

6. Relative heat capacities of silver and aluminum.

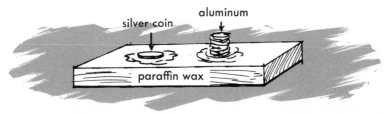

Remove coin from boiling water. Quickly dry and lay it on the paraffin. Do same with aluminum. Wait about 15 minutes, then pry each from the paraffin.

Which melted more paraffin? Compare the size of the cavities in the paraffin. Which has a greater heat capacity, weight for weight, silver or aluminum?

7. Try similar experiments with equal weights of lead and aluminum or any two different metals.

facts and ideas about . . .

Ice at Its Melting Point

You are going to cool ice below the freezing temperature of water. To do this you will place a tray of ice cubes in the freezing compartment of your refrigerator. After about a half-hour your ice cubes will be at the temperature of the freezer.

If the temperature of the freezing compartment is 20° Fahrenheit, then the ice cubes will be cooled to 20° Fahrenheit. Why? You will observe that these ice cubes do not begin melting immediately on being removed from the freezer. Melting will not begin until the air in the room has warmed the surfaces of the ice cubes to 32° F, the melting point of ice. Why?

You will crush a few of the ice cubes and place the small pieces in a cup or glass. Check the temperature of the melting crushed ice with your thermometer. Can you get the temperature of the melting crushed ice to rise above 32° F by adding a few tablespoons of room temperature water? By adding a little hot water? Try it.

Remember that ice melts at a definite or fixed temperature. Applying heat will make the ice melt faster — but the temperature of the ice-and-water mixture will stay at 32° F until all the ice has melted.

The melting point and freezing point of a solid are the same. This means that ice for example, melts at exactly the same temperature as water freezes. This temperature is 32° F or 0° C.

You will observe that the temperature of ice cannot be raised above 32° F, its melting point, no matter how fast you add heat to the ice. After *all the ice* has melted, however, the addition of heat will raise the

temperature of the *water* formed from the ice above 32° F. Why?
Definition: By melting point is meant the temperature at which a solid changes to a liquid, or a liquid to a solid, under *normal* atmospheric pressure. Every solid has its own melting point. Here are the melting points of several common substances:

ice	0° C	aluminum	658° C
mercury	−39° C	lead	327° C
sulphur	114° C	copper	1080° C

(See page 25 on how to convert centigrade to Fahrenheit:)

Notes on the experiments that follow: Be sure to stir your ice-and-water mixture or your results may prove confusing. The heat of the room may raise the temperature of the unstirred water and thus give unexpected thermometer readings.

About thermometers: The best thermometer to use in these experiments is the mercury-in-glass type or laboratory thermometer. It costs about $2 and may obtained from a laboratory supply house by mail order. See list of laboratory supply companies and addresses on page 89. The range of laboratory thermometers varies; for your purposes a range of −20° F to 220° F will be satisfactory. If you cannot get a laboratory type thermometer, buy *two* low-priced thermometers at a ten-cent or hardware store: one, called an indoor-outdoor thermometer, will have a range of about −30° F to 120° F; the other, called a candy thermometer, will have a range of about 100° F to 400° F.

How Ice Behaves at Its Melting Point

A freezing compartment of your refrigerator

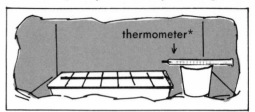

DO THIS: Place a thermometer in the freezing compartment of a refrigerator. Lay it alongside a tray of ice cubes. Leave thermometer in the closed compartment for a half hour.

Now remove thermometer and *quickly* read its temperature. Suppose it reads 20° F. This means that the ice cubes are at 20° F.

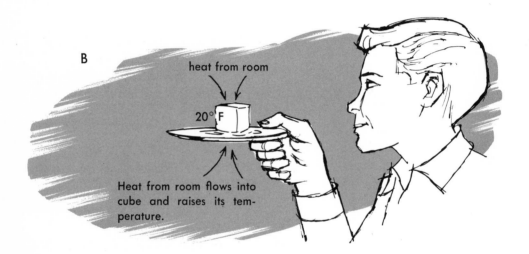

B

heat from room

20° F

Heat from room flows into cube and raises its temperature.

Remove ice tray. Examine cubes immediately. Is the ice dry? Observe cubes carefully for a few minutes.

Do the ice cubes become *wet* at the surface? If so, then the heat from the room has warmed the outside of the cubes to 32° F, the melting point of ice.

* See note on the type of thermometer to buy, etc. on p. 37.

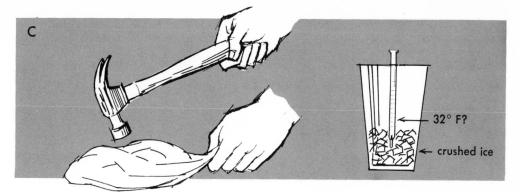

Place a few cubes in a towel and crush, using hammer or any weight.

What is the temperature of the slowly melting crushed ice?

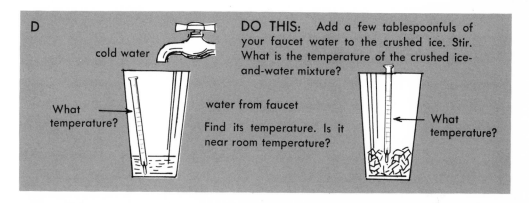

DO THIS: Add a few tablespoonfuls of your faucet water to the crushed ice. Stir. What is the temperature of the crushed ice-and-water mixture?

cold water

What temperature?

water from faucet

Find its temperature. Is it near room temperature?

What temperature?

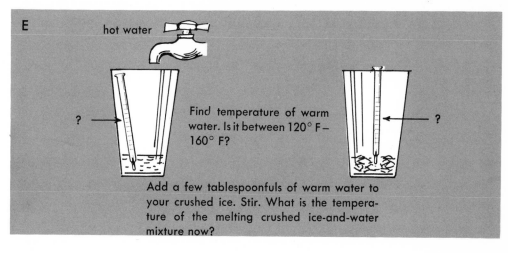

hot water

?

Find temperature of warm water. Is it between 120° F – 160° F?

?

Add a few tablespoonfuls of warm water to your crushed ice. Stir. What is the temperature of the melting crushed ice-and-water mixture now?

facts and ideas about . . .

The Expansion of Water on Freezing

You are going to try to get an approximate measure of the increase in volume when water changes to ice.

To do this you will make use of the spaces or compartments in an ordinary ice tray. First you will mark off, as directed, the depth of water in two different compartments. Then you will measure the change in depth after the water solidifies into an ice cube.

You may start with water from your cold-water faucet. However, for accurate determinations, it is best to make the first measurement with water at 4° centigrade (39° Fahrenheit). Why? Because water at this temperature has contracted to its minimum value. In other words, water is at its maximum density at 4° centigrade.

We all know that ice floats in water. Therefore ice must weigh less than an *equal volume* of water. Tests have proven that 100 cubic inches of water will occupy 109 cubic inches when changed to ice at 0° C (32° F).

This is another way of saying that water expands 9% when it freezes — i.e., it increases by one-eleventh of its original volume when it solidifies. Think about this.

Type used for printing is made of metals which *expand* when they solidify. Otherwise the outline of each letter will be indistinct. Type metal is an alloy of lead, antimony, and copper. The molten type metal is poured into molds. As the liquid type metal solidifies it expands against the sides of the mold. The result is a clear, sharp outline of the letter.

Unlike water and type metal, most substances *contract* when they freeze or solidify, and *expand* when they melt or liquefy. Gold and silver coins, for example, cannot be *cast:* they will not assume the exact shape and design of a mold on solidifying. Why? Coins of these metals must therefore be *stamped*.

Notice the surface of a dish of gelatin dessert which has been allowed to solidify in your refrigerator. Is the center of the gelatin raised or depressed? Does gelatin expand or contract on solidifying?

Does paraffin wax behave like water or like *most metals* on changing from a liquid to a solid? Try the experiment on the next page before answering.

Did it occur to you that the aluminum compartment itself, in your experiment, contracted as it cooled off in the refrigerator? If so, then this contraction of the aluminum form must have pushed the water and ice up higher in the compartment. It is true that the aluminum shell contracted, but only to the extent of a few parts per million. The expansion of ice is much greater than this figure — i.e., 9 parts per hundred.

This difficulty, caused by the expanding or contracting of the container itself, is always troublesome in expansion experiments. The experimenter must remember that what he measures is usually *relative* or *differential* expansion. Do you see why this is so?

Expansion of Water on Freezing

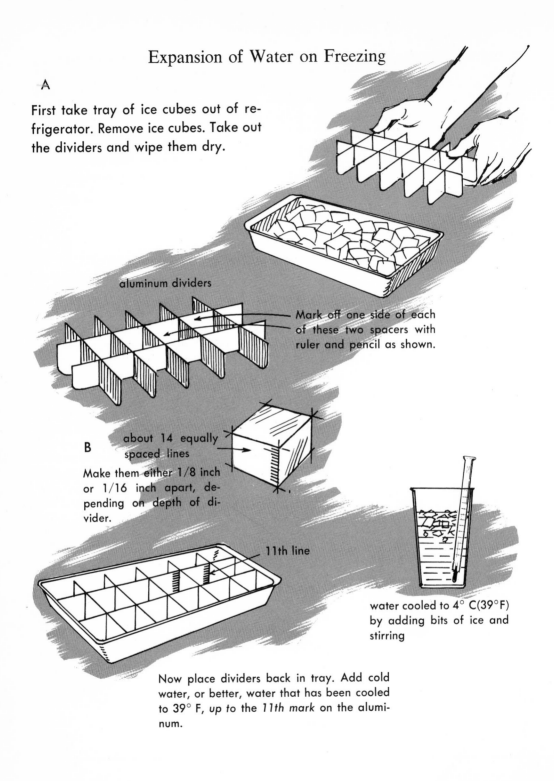

A

First take tray of ice cubes out of refrigerator. Remove ice cubes. Take out the dividers and wipe them dry.

aluminum dividers

Mark off one side of each of these two spacers with ruler and pencil as shown.

B

about 14 equally spaced lines

Make them either 1/8 inch or 1/16 inch apart, depending on depth of divider.

11th line

water cooled to 4° C(39°F) by adding bits of ice and stirring

Now place dividers back in tray. Add cold water, or better, water that has been cooled to 39° F, *up to* the *11th mark* on the aluminum.

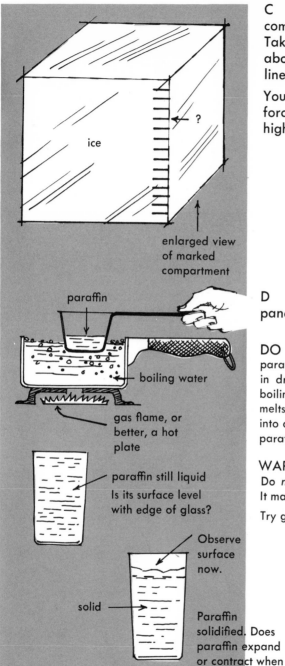

C Carefully place tray in freezing compartment until water freezes solid. Take out and examine. Is ice level above the line 11 mark? How many lines higher?

You will have to estimate this because force of expansion makes ice cube higher in center of compartment.

paraffin

ice

?

enlarged view of marked compartment

boiling water

gas flame, or better, a hot plate

paraffin still liquid

Is its surface level with edge of glass?

Observe surface now.

solid

Paraffin solidified. Does paraffin expand or contract when it freezes?

D To find out if *all* substances expand on solidification,

DO THIS: Take about 1/2 cake of the paraffin wax used for sealing fruit jars. Place in dry saucepan. Set this pan in a pot of boiling water as shown. Wait until paraffin melts completely. Then pour melted paraffin into a small glass right up to its rim. Wait till paraffin solidifies. Examine it.

WARNING:
Do *not* heat paraffin directly over a flame. It may catch fire.

Try gelatin for safety.

facts and ideas about . . .

The Behavior of Ice under Pressure

You are going to press two ice cubes together to find out if pressure will cause them to melt more readily. More precisely, the question is this: Does pressure have any effect on the melting temperature, or melting point, of ice?

Suppose you find that the extra pressure causes the ice to melt at the points of contact. We may then conclude that pressure lowers the melting point of ice. Why? Because the ice, which is at 32° F, apparently cannot stay in a solid state *above* its *new* melting point. This *new* melting point must therefore be *lower* than the *old* (32° F) melting point. Why?

When the pressure on the ice cubes is released, the melting point changes back to 0° C or 32° F. The film of water that had formed between the two ice cubes freezes solid immediately. Why? Because its temperature is below 32° F, which is the freezing temperature of water under normal atmospheric pressure. Think about this.

The fact that pressure lowers the melting point of ice was discovered in the middle of the nineteenth century. It has been found that a pressure increase of one atmosphere (14.7 lbs. per square inch) will lower the melting point of ice .0075° C.

When you pack snow tightly in making a snowball, the pressure you apply causes the melting point to become lower than the temperature of the snow. As a result some of the snow melts. When you stop pressing the snow together the melted portion freezes and holds the snowball together. Why is it difficult to make a snowball on a very cold day, when the temperature is far below 32° F? Why does the snow seem "dry" after pressing?

Pressure does not lower the melting point of all substances. Some, like paraffin which contracts on solidification, will melt at a higher temperature when outside pressure is applied. In other words, pressure makes it more difficult to melt this class of substances.

The experiment you will make with the weighted thin wire cutting through ice demonstrates *regelation*. Regelation is the name given to the process of melting under pressure and freezing again after the pressure has been removed.

What has regelation to do with ice skating? As you skate on ice the weight of your body causes the skate blade to press against the ice with considerable force. This pressure, if the temperature is not too low, will melt the ice under the blade. This layer of water then acts as a lubricant for your blade. Once the pressure is removed, the layer of water immediately refreezes. Why?

The flow of glaciers is explained to some extent by regelation. The weight of the ice mass causes melting near the bottom because the pressure is great there. As this water flows out from the lower part of the glacier it soon freezes again because the pressure on it has been reduced.

Pressure Causes Ice to Melt

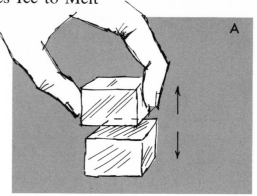

DO THIS: Take two ice cubes. Place one on the other. Now separate them. Try sliding one over the other. Do they come apart easily?

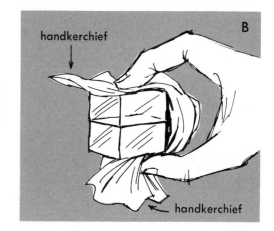

Now press these same ice cubes together firmly for 5 to 10 seconds. Do they stick together now? Do they seem to have frozen together?

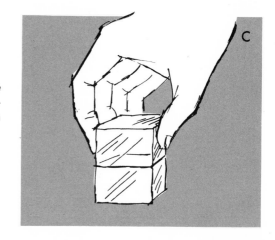

Will upper cube hold up lower one? Examine points where the two cubes meet. What happened to layer of moisture that was between the contact surface at first?

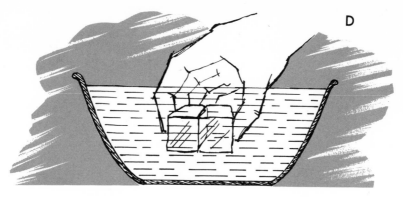

D

Try pressing ice cubes together while they are in bowl of warm water. Do they stick together while in the bowl? When taken out?

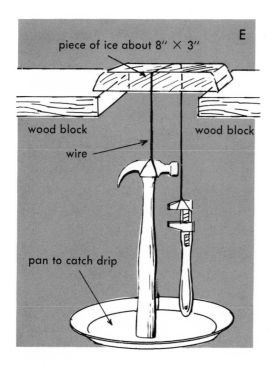

E

piece of ice about 8" × 3"

wood block   wood block

wire

pan to catch drip

Try this experiment:

1. Freeze an ice tray full of water (without dividers).

2. Remove the ice and arrange ice, thin wire, weights, wood supports, as in diagram.

3. Examine after 10 or 15 minutes. Does wire cut through ice? What happens in "cut" above wire? Does cut remain open? Or does it close up again at end of experiment? Do you have one piece of ice or two?

facts and ideas about . . .

Freezing Mixtures

You are going to dissolve common salt in water and then add ordinary ice cubes to this salt water. You will thus make a *freezing mixture*. Can you lower the temperature of your mixture *below* the freezing point of water, that is, below 0° C or 32° F?

Do you recall the experiment where you mixed ice with pure water (see page 36)? When you did this the temperature of the mixture dropped to the freezing point of water, 0° C or 32° F, and stayed at that temperature until *all the ice* had melted.

The freezing point of salt water — that is, of salt solution — is *lower* than that of pure water. The more salt you dissolve in water, the *lower* the freezing point of the solution.

The freezing point of water is usually lowered when substances are dissolved in it. Do you see why motorists add alcohol, ethylene glycol, etc., to the radiators of their cars in winter? What is the advantage of a *lower* freezing point for the liquid in the car radiator?

You will try to freeze brine, or dilute salt solution, in your refrigerator. If you can get the ice to separate from the solution, be sure to taste this ice. Is it salt-free, slightly salty, or very salty? Try it.

To freeze ice cream at home you place the ice-cream can in a container of cracked ice and salt. A good proportion to use is three parts of cracked ice to one part of common salt.

What happens? Heat from the ice-cream can or from the air in the room melts some of the ice. The water thus formed dissolves some of the salt. The salt solution has a lower freezing point than pure water. The salt solution-and-ice mixture drops to the freezing point of the solution. Heat passes into this mixture from the ice-cream can. More ice melts. The ice cream gets colder and colder and finally freezes.

You will try sprinkling salt over an ice cube which has not begun to melt. Does the cube remain dry? Explain. Remember that the salt solution on the surface of the ice cube has a lower freezing point than pure water. Try to explain why salt sprinkled on icy sidewalks brings about the melting of the ice.

The concentration of salt in sea water varies in different parts of the world. The average is about three parts per hundred or 3%. The temperature of sea water must fall to $-2°$ C (28.4° F) *at least* before ice will separate from sea water.

The ice which separates from sea water will contain only about one-fifth of the salt originally present in the sea water. This fact is the basis of methods used to extract salt from sea water in the colder regions of the world.

Basins full of sea water are exposed to very cold air. The crust of ice which forms is then removed. This leaves a more concentrated salt solution in the basin. The process is continued until the salt water becomes so concentrated that it is ready for boiling. The boiling process removes the remaining water, leaving dry salt. Try it on a day when the out-of-door temperature is well below freezing.

Freezing Mixtures

A

DO THIS: Take two glasses. Half fill each with water. Add 1 teaspoonful of salt to one glass and stir till dissolved. Let stand till water in each glass is at room temperature.

faucet water   salt water

B

DO THIS: Add 3 or 4 ice cubes to each glass and stir. Does the pure water temperature fall to 32° F as before? Is the temperature of the salt water-and-ice mixture lower than 32° F? Try adding more salt to the salt-water glass. Does temperature fall still more on stirring?

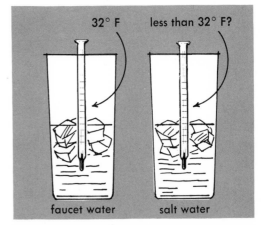

32° F   less than 32° F?

faucet water   salt water

C

TRY THIS: Add 1 teaspoonful of salt to 1/2 glass of water as before. Pour some of the solution into a saucer which you will place in freezing compartment of your refrigerator for one hour. Does salt water freeze? Taste the ice as soon as it forms. Is it salty? Taste the water. Is it salty? Find temperature of mixture while it is still in freezer.

salt water in freezing compartment

taste the ice   taste the water

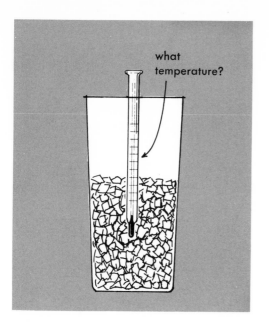

what temperature?

D Try a freezing mixture of ice and salt such as is used in making ice cream at home. Add 1 part ordinary salt to 3 parts of crushed ice. Use a tablespoon for measuring.
Does the addition of salt make the ice melt? Feel the outside of the glass. Is the temperature of the mixture below 32° F? How many degrees below?

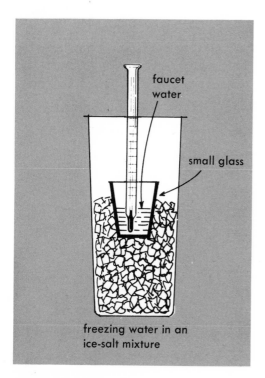

faucet water

small glass

freezing water in an ice-salt mixture

E Set a small glass, with 1/2 inch of water in it, in the above salt-ice mixture. Stir water with thermometer. Does the water in the inner glass become cold enough to solidify?

F TRY THIS: Take an ice cube and dry it carefully with towel. Sprinkle salt on ice cube. Does ice cube become "wet"? Why? Try sprinkling salt on dry ice cube while it is in the freezing compartment. Any melting observed? Explain.

facts and ideas about . . .

The Cooling Effect of Evaporation

If a liquid at room temperature is allowed to evaporate slowly in an open dish, will the liquid become cooler? You will find out by testing a saucer of water and a saucer of alcohol in the experiment described on the next page. You will compare the drop in temperature when water evaporates with the drop in temperature when alcohol evaporates.

Definition: Evaporation is the changing of a liquid to a gas or vapor. When the vapor molecules are quickly carried away by air currents, evaporation continues until all of the liquid has changed to a vapor. Do you see why a dish of water, exposed to the air, eventually becomes dry?

Suppose the water or alcohol is in a closed container — i.e., a stoppered bottle? Some of the liquid molecules escape and enter the space in the bottle above the liquid. As this space becomes crowded with these molecules, some of them plunge back into the liquid. When as many molecules leave as return to the liquid we say the vapor is *saturated:* it has in it as many vapor molecules as it can hold at the existing temperature.

You will read the temperature of a thermometer before moistening its bulb with water. You will read the thermometer temperature after moistening the bulb with water at room temperature. Will the evaporating water cool the bulb? Try it. You will repeat this experiment using alcohol instead of water. Be sure to dry the bulb well before proceeding in each case.

You will moisten one of your wrists with water and the other with alcohol. Both liquids will be at the same temperature. Which wrist will feel cooler? Try it. Do you see why a person with a fever is rubbed with alcohol rather than with water?

Water may be kept cool by storing it in canvas bags or in unglazed earthenware vessels. Some water is lost by evaporation through the canvas or earthenware. Can you explain why water keeps cool under these conditions?

Your body loses a pint to a quart of water per day in the form of perspiration. What is the effect on the body temperature of the evaporation of this moisture? How does the body keep the evaporation process from lowering the body temperature below 98.6° F?

What is the explanation of the cooling effect of evaporation? According to the kinetic theory the molecules of a liquid are in constant random motion. As the result of collisions some of the molecules acquire high velocities momentarily. These high-speed molecules occasionally break away from the attraction of neighboring molecules and fly off into the space above the liquid.

The loss of these rapidly moving molecules lowers the temperature of the liquid. Why? Because the average velocity of the molecules left behind becomes *less*. Therefore the temperature of the liquid falls. Think about this. Remember that temperature is an indication or measure of the average activity of the molecules of a substance.

The Cooling Effect of Evaporation

A

DO THIS: Let bottles stand alongside each other for about an hour. The temperature of each liquid will then be the same as the temperature of the air in the room. Check room temperature with a thermometer. Then find the temperature of the water and the alcohol.

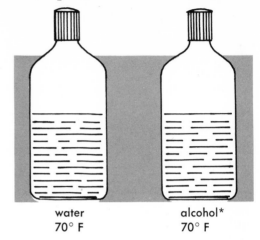

water
70° F

alcohol*
70° F

air in room 70° F

(Yours may be different. It doesn't matter as long as you know what the temperature is.)

B

Pour a little water into one saucer and about the same quantity of alcohol into another saucer. Place clean, dry thermometer bulb in each.

Did temperature drop in each saucer — as compared with bottle temperature found earlier?

Which cooled off more in open dish — the water or the alcohol? Why? Which liquid evaporates faster?

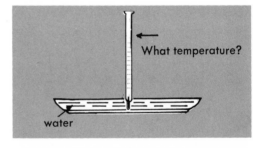

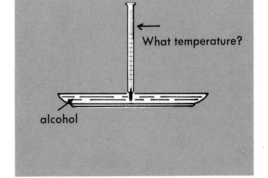

* You may use ordinary rubbing alcohol in this experiment.

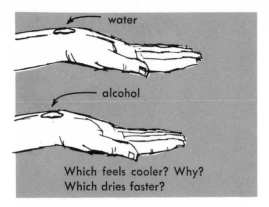

water

alcohol

Which feels cooler? Why?
Which dries faster?

C Try moistening one of your wrists with water and the other with alcohol. Be sure both liquids are at the same temperature.

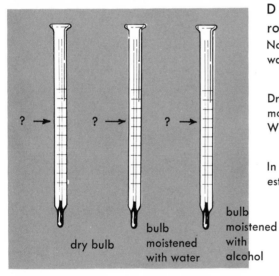

? →   ? →   ? →

dry bulb

bulb moistened with water

bulb moistened with alcohol

D Hold a thermometer up and read room temperature.
Now moisten the bulb with room temperature water. After 2 minutes read thermometer.

Dry the bulb, wait two minutes, and then moisten bulb with room temperature alcohol. Wait 2 minutes and then read thermometer.

In which case is temperature highest? Lowest? Explain.

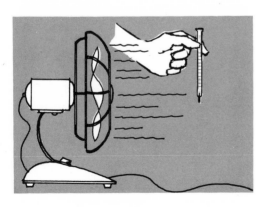

E Repeat the above but this time hold thermometer in front of an electric fan; or fan the thermometer bulb with a cardboard.

Does fan cause temperature to drop more or less than in previous experiment? Why?

Dew Point

You are going to cool a tightly-covered glass of ordinary air. Will the air within the glass lose some of its water vapor by condensation as the result of cooling?

Condensation is the changing of a vapor or gas into its liquid. If it were not for the condensation of the water vapor in the air we would live in an atmosphere saturated with water vapor. Why? Because the evaporation of water from rivers, lakes, and oceans is continually going on. Think about this.

You will also try the above experiment with air to which you have added an extra amount of water vapor. Do you think this additional water vapor will quickly condense inside the glass on cooling? Try it.

Remember that the warmer the air the greater the amount of water vapor it can hold. *Water vapor* is the name given to water when it is in the form of an invisible gas. Do you see why cooling helps to remove water vapor from air?

The amount of water vapor present in the air or atmosphere is called *absolute humidity*. It is usually expressed as the number of *grains* of water per cubic foot of air, or as the number of grams of water per cubic meter of air. (One pound avoirdupois contains 7000 grains.)

The amount of water vapor in the atmosphere varies from day to day, sometimes from hour to hour. When air contains little or no water vapor, we say the air is dry. When air contains much water vapor, we say the air is damp.

The *dew point* is the temperature to which the atmosphere must be cooled before the water vapor within will *begin* to condense. Note that in your dew-point experiment you will be concerned with the air *outside* the container; that is, the air surrounding, and close to, the vessel into which you will drop bits of ice.

In other words, you will be cooling the air next to the cold container. When this air is cooled to a temperature at which it becomes saturated with water vapor, further cooling will cause this air to deposit some of its moisture on the outside of the cold container. Think about this.

When we say air is saturated with water vapor, we mean that this particular air has within it as much vapor as it can hold at the given temperature. Any further cooling will lead to the condensation of excess moisture on the wall or sides of the cold container.

In order for rain or snow to form, the atmosphere must be cooled *below* its dew point. If the dew point is above freezing (0° C or 32° F), rain will fall as the result of condensation. If the dew point is below freezing temperature, snow will fall. Why?

We are usually interested not in the *absolute humidity* of air but rather in the relative dampness or *relative humidity* of the air. Relative humidity is the ratio between the amount of moisture air has in it and the amount which would be present if the air were saturated at the current temperature.

Dew Point

A

DO THIS: Take clean dry glass. Cover it tightly, perhaps with thin plastic wrapping. Does this air contain water vapor?

B

Let's cool it to make the water vapor come out in the form of a mist (condensation).

Air is at room temperature.
Note the temperature.

Set the above sealed glass of air in the freezing compartment of a refrigerator. Examine after 1/2 hour. Has any moisture appeared *inside* the glass? Examine the *underside* of the plastic cover.

Invert a clean dry glass in a saucer of warm water (about 100° F) for 5 minutes.

clear air but with much water vapor in it

Remove glass. Quickly wipe dry. Cover with plastic again.

C

Now try the above experiment with air containing much water vapor.

Observe glass after covering it tightly. Does it stay dry inside? Wait five minutes. Try placing it in freezer for 1/2 hour. Examine it. Any mist or drops of water *inside* after cooling? Explain.

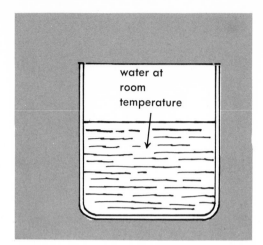

water at
room
temperature

D

Dew Point. Let's find the exact temperature at which the moisture in the atmosphere will condense on the *outside* of a glass or metal container.

saucer of
ice chips

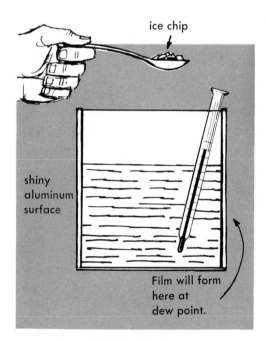

ice chip

shiny
aluminum
surface

Film will form
here at
dew point.

DO THIS: Get a polished metal can, or use a glass with a *thin* layer of shiny aluminum foil wrapped around it.

Add an ice chip and stir liquid with thermometer. Do you see a film of moisture on the outside of the container? If not, add another chip. Stir. Look for moisture film. Keep this up until a film appears. Now read the temperature *quickly*. This temperature is the *Dew Point* of the air in your room at the time you did the experiment.

Check by repeating the above. Average your results. Work carefully.

facts and ideas about . . .

Boiling

You are going to boil water in an open pan. Your thermometer will indicate the exact temperature at which water boils under normal atmospheric pressure. Normal atmospheric pressure is 14.7 lbs. per square inch.

You will increase the pressure on the surface of the boiling water slightly by covering the pan *loosely* with a large plate. Does the boiling temperature change when the outside pressure is increased? Try it.

You are going to dissolve a substance like salt in the water and then heat this salt water until it boils.Will your salt water boil at the same temperature as pure water? Try it.

You will notice that when a liquid boils, rapid evaporation takes place *both* at the surface *and* in the interior of the liquid. You will observe steam bubbles rising from *within* the water itself during boiling.

A liquid, when heated, will of course get warmer and warmer. However, this is true only up to a certain temperature. This temperature, above which the liquid cannot be raised when the pressure is *constant*, is called the *boiling temperature*. In other words, once a liquid is actively boiling, its temperature remains the same no matter how rapidly heat is applied.

The boiling temperature of pure water under normal atmospheric pressure is 100° C or 212° F. In a closed container equipped with a safety valve, like the ordinary pressure cooker, the temperature of boiling water will be considerably *higher* than 100° C or 212° F. Why?

For example, if the pressure on the boiling water inside the cooker is

24.55 lbs. per square inch, the temperature of the boiling water will be 115° C or 239° F. Do you see why a pressure cooker reduces cooking time?

In general, dissolving a solid in a liquid raises the boiling point. In the case of salt solution, the boiling point may be raised to 108° C if enough salt is added to saturate the water. Why is a pinch of salt often added to water in which food is cooked?

Different substances boil at different temperatures. Here are a few boiling points of common substances when the pressure is normal, or 14.7 lbs. per square inch: (See page 25 about conversion of centigrade temperature to Fahrenheit.)

grain alcohol	78° C	gasoline	75° — 80° C
turpentine	160° C	lead	1620° C
mercury	357° C	iron	3000° C

At high altitudes, as you may suspect, water boils at a *lower* temperature than at sea level. Why? Because the higher you go above the surface of the earth the less pressure of the atmosphere. For every 1000 feet above sea level the boiling point drops about 1° C.

At the summit of Pikes Peak, for example, water boils at 89° C or 192° F. How would you solve the cooking problem there? In the manufacture of sugar, water is removed from the syrup by boiling it under reduced pressure. Why?

Boiling

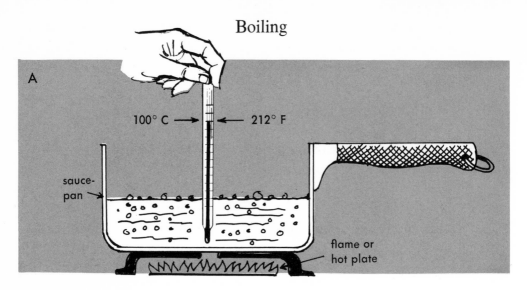

100° C → ← 212° F

sauce-pan

flame or hot plate

DO THIS: Half fill a saucepan with water. Heat until it boils. Take temperature of the boiling water. Did you see small air bubbles rising from the water while it was warmed?

Did you see steam bubbles rising while water was boiling? Does the temperature rise when the water is made to boil *more* vigorously?

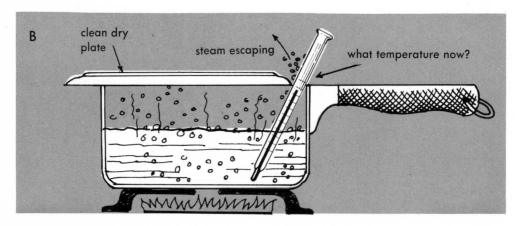

clean dry plate

steam escaping

what temperature now?

Set a dry clean dinner plate *loosely* over saucepan. Be sure steam can escape between plate and thermometer. Does a slight pressure build up under plate when water begins

to boil? Does this extra pressure change the thermometer reading from what it was in the open pan — i.e., 100° C or 212° F? Find out. Can you explain your results?

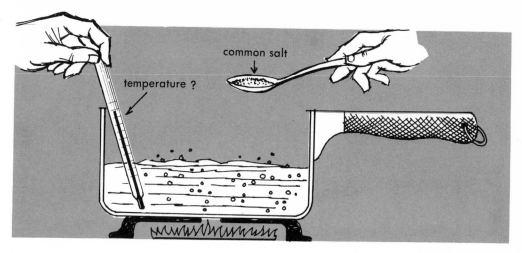

C While water is boiling in open pan, add 1 teaspoonful of salt. Notice that the boiling stops for a few moments and then resumes.

Read the temperature of the boiling salt water. Is it higher than that of pure water? Why? Repeat, using a teaspoonful of *sugar* instead of salt.

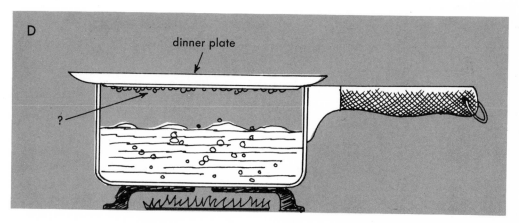

Set your pan of salt water to boiling once more. Place a large dry dinner plate loosely over the pan. After a few minutes remove plate, using pot holder to grip it.

Are there drops of water hanging on underside of plate? Taste these drops. Are they salty? Explain. You have produced a few drops of distilled water by this method. Explain.

facts and ideas about . . .

Conduction of Heat

You are going to place small pieces of different materials in the freezing compartment of a refrigerator. You will leave them there until all have reached the same temperature — the temperature of the freezing compartment. Will the copper, silver, wood, paper, and so forth, all feel equally cold to your fingers? Why not — since they are all at the same temperature? Try it.

The more rapidly a substance conducts heat from your hand, the the colder the substance *feels*. Why will copper, for example, feel colder than paper even when both are at exactly the same temperature? Try it at room temperature, too. Remember that hot and cold are sensations. Your sense organs may indicate a difference in temperature when no such difference exists. Do you see why one must depend on a thermometer rather than on sensations in judging temperatures?

The more rapidly an object conducts heat to your hand, the hotter the object will feel to you. Suppose you should take a hot cake pan out of an oven carelessly. Why will the burn be more severe if you touch the pan than if you touch the cake? Both, of course, are at the same temperature.

Heat is commonly spoken of as *flowing* from a place of high temperature to one of low temperature. Keep in mind that heat does not actually flow, for it is not a fluid. Heat is a form of energy.

The transfer of heat through a substance from molecule to molecule is called *conduction*. When your finger touches a cold object, heat is conveyed from your warmer finger to the colder object. The molecules in your finger slow down and you experience the sensation of cold. At the same time, the heat that passes from your finger into the cold object makes its molecules vibrate more rapidly. What change takes place in the temperature of the cold object? Why?

Suppose you touch a hot object — for example, one whose molecules have been stirred or agitated into greater vibration by the heat of a flame. Will heat be conducted into your finger or out of it? Explain.

Will a strip of thin paper wrapped tightly around a metal rod be scorched when held in a flame for a few seconds? The metal rod is a good conductor of heat. Will it conduct the heat away so rapidly that the paper will not get hot enough to be scorched? Try it. Suppose you use a poor conductor like a wooden rod in this same experiment. Will the paper be scorched this time? Try it. Can you explain your results?

Copper-wire gauze, that is, fine copper screening, will conduct heat away from a flame so rapidly that very little heat from the flame will pass through the screening. In your experiment try holding your hand as close to the flame and above it as comfort permits. Now place the copper screening between the flame and your hand. Do you feel more heat or less heat now? Do you see why fine copper gauze is used in the famous Davy safety lamp?

Conduction of Heat

A

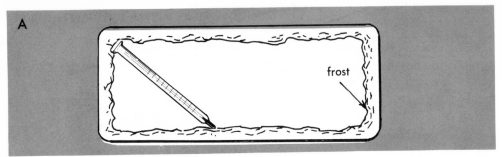

frost

Place a thermometer in the freezing compartment of your refrigerator. Close door of refrigerator. After 5 minutes open door and read thermometer *while* it is in freezing compartment. The temperature should be below 32° F — at least 5° below the freezing point.

B

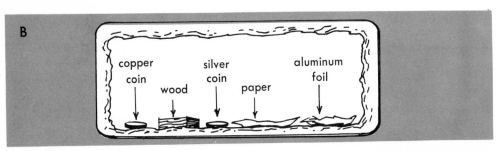

copper coin   silver coin   aluminum foil

wood   paper

Place five different materials, as shown, on the frost at bottom of freezing compartment. Shut refrigerator door. Wait 5 minutes. Now open door and touch each substance lightly with *different* finger. Do the metals feel colder than the paper or wood? Which feels colder, the paper or the wood?

In which cases does substance stick to finger? Why?

C   Have you ever noticed how a moistened finger sticks to cold metals on icy days? Moisten a different finger each time and touch each substance in the freezing compartment.

WARNING: If metal sticks to finger too firmly, do *not* pull it away. Apply warm water and metal will separate from finger painlessly.

Get a piece of copper screening about 4" × 6". Support as shown. Place two pieces of paper near middle. Place another on edge of screening so that part of paper hangs over edge.

Light candle. Place flame under inside bits of paper. Do they catch fire? Feel screening. Is it hot? Place flame under overhanging part of paper. Does it burn? Does part resting on screen burn too? Explain.

D

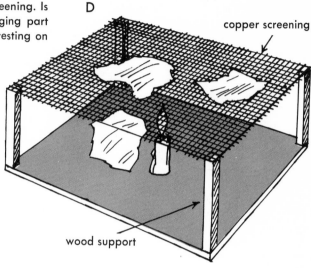

copper screening

wood support

E

Wrap a piece of thin paper spiral fashion once around a copper rod. Hold part where there is only one thickness over candle flame. Does paper catch fire? Wipe off carbon from paper and examine.

Try same with wooden rod. Does paper burn this time? Which is a better conductor of heat — copper or wood?

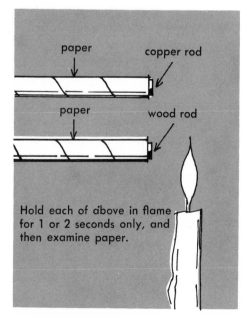

paper   copper rod

paper   wood rod

Hold each of above in flame for 1 or 2 seconds only, and then examine paper.

facts and ideas about . . .

Heat Conductivity

You are going to compare the heat conductivity of iron with that of copper. In other words, you will compare the rate of flow of heat through these conductors.

In your experiment you will place one end of an iron rod in boiling water alongside a similar copper rod. Each rod will have drops of paraffin wax at half-inch intervals along its exposed length. As the heat is conducted from the warmer to the cooler parts of each rod, some of the drops of wax will melt. Will the same number of drops melt on each rod? Try it.

Since some metals take longer to heat than others (see p. 32 on Specific Heat), it is important that you wait several minutes after the melting of the drops stops and a steady-state is reached. This means that no further temperature change along the rods is taking place. In this way, the fact that some metals heat up faster than others will not invalidate your experiment. Can you explain the last statement?

The idea for this experiment was suggested by Benjamin Franklin (1706-1790), the American statesman and scientist. An experiment of this kind was first made in 1789. Several rods of different metals were used. One end of each was inserted in a pot of boiling oil; the rods were coated with beeswax.

More accurate experiments carried out later established a number, or factor, called thermal conductivity, for each material. This number tells us how much heat, measured in calories (see page 29), is conducted per second through a layer of a substance 1 centimeter thick and across an area of 1 square centimeter when the temperature difference is 1 centigrade degree.

The thermal or heat conductivities of a few common substances are:

silver	0.99	glass	0.002	asbestos (sheets)	
copper	0.91	ice	0.005		0.0004
aluminum	0.49	snow	0.0011	water	0.0015
iron	0.16	paper	0.0003	air	0.000054
sand (white, dry)		silk	0.000095		
	0.0009				

Do you see why freshly fallen snow protects vegetation? Why loosely woven fabrics, full of trapped air, are good insulators? Poor conductors of heat such as asbestos, rockwool, sawdust, fiberglass, felt, and powdered cork are called *heat insulators*.

To show that water is a poor conductor of heat you will try to float a bit of ice in a coffee-can cover containing water that is boiling a few inches from where the ice is. Liquids are relatively poor conductors of heat. Gases are even poorer conductors than liquids: for example, gases on the average have a heat conductivity of about $\frac{1}{25}$ that of water.

Metals in general conduct heat better than other solids. Silver is the best conductor of heat; mercury, which is liquid at ordinary temperatures, is the poorest conductor among the common metals. Keep in mind that all metals, even though they vary in conductivity, are *good* conductors of heat.

Interesting facts: (a) Good conductors of heat are also good conductors of electricity (b) Aluminum (0.49) is a good conductor of heat; but when aluminum foil is crumpled to form $\frac{3}{8}$-inch air spaces it becomes a good heat insulator (0.0001). Why?

Heat Conductivity

1.

Get a copper guide rod at hardware store. Straighten loop with pliers.

Find a wire coat-hanger of the same thickness as the copper rod. Cut off piece of same length as copper rod. Sandpaper the iron rod lightly.

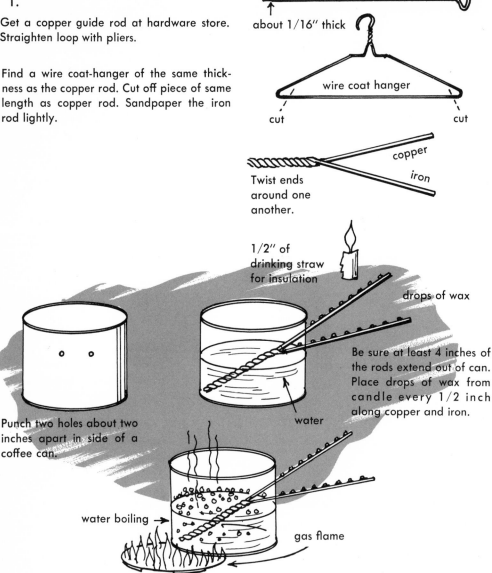

copper guide rod about 8″ long

about 1/16″ thick

wire coat hanger

cut   cut

Twist ends around one another.

copper

iron

1/2″ of drinking straw for insulation

drops of wax

Be sure at least 4 inches of the rods extend out of can. Place drops of wax from candle every 1/2 inch along copper and iron.

water

Punch two holes about two inches apart in side of a coffee can.

water boiling

gas flame

Flame is at edge of can to keep its heat as far as possible from the extending part of the rods. Use low flame to boil the water.

When a drop of wax melts it flattens out or slides under the rod. After about ten minutes, and when *no further melting* of wax occurs, turn flame off. Let rods cool for five minutes. Which metal has higher heat conductivity? Why did heat stop flowing through rods to more distant points? Is this method better than attaching tacks to rods with wax? Explain.

2. Water has a low heat conductivity.

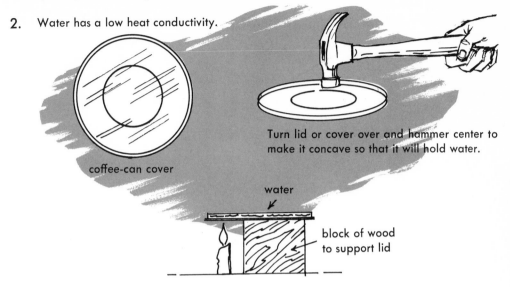

coffee-can cover

Turn lid or cover over and hammer center to make it concave so that it will hold water.

water

block of wood to support lid

about 1/4" of water in lid

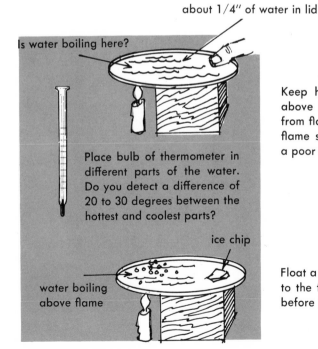

Is water boiling here?

Place bulb of thermometer in different parts of the water. Do you detect a difference of 20 to 30 degrees between the hottest and coolest parts?

ice chip

water boiling above flame

Keep heating with candle flame till water above flame boils. Touch water at far end from flame with finger. Move finger closer to flame side. Explain the difference. Is water a poor conductor of heat?

Float a few ice chips in the water. How close to the flame side can you move an ice chip before it melts rapidly? Try it.

facts and ideas about . . .

Convection

You are going to investigate the transfer of heat through water. What you find out in regard to water will also be true of fluids in general, that is, all liquids and gases.

By means of a straw you will carefully introduce a few drops of ink in the bottom of a jar of water. The movement of the inky layer will enable you to see how the water circulates when its temperature changes. What happens when a jar of hot water is cooled at the bottom? When a jar of cold water is heated at the bottom? When a jar of hot water is cooled at the top? Try it. In which of these arrangements are mixing or *convection* currents produced? Why?

What is convection? Convection is the transfer of heat by a *moving* substance; that is, the warmer particles of a fluid mix with the colder particles. Convection occurs when a liquid or gas is heated at the *bottom* or cooled at the *top*. Why? Heat expands fluids and makes them less dense. Cooling causes fluids to contract and become more dense. Do you see why it makes a difference, where convection is concerned, whether a liquid is heated at the bottom or at the top? Explain.

Water, like most liquids, is a poor conductor of heat. Why, then, can one heat a pan of water over a flame so quickly to a fairly uniform temperature? The answer is that the heat from the flame is transferred through the water by convection. The process is as follows: the water at the bottom of the pan becomes warm first; heat makes it expand and become less dense, that is, lighter, than the surrounding colder water. What happens next? The heavier colder water flows under the warm water and pushes it up from the bottom. This cold water, on being heated, rises in turn, and so forth. In this way a continuous stirring or circulation of the water takes place while it is being heated.

You will try floating a few ice cubes in a jar of hot water. The inky layer at the bottom will reveal convection currents — if any are produced. Will the cooling of a liquid at the top cause convection currents in the liquid? Try it. Can you explain your results?

The water in hot-water tanks is heated by convection. Winds are convection currents in the atmosphere caused by the unequal heating of the surface of the earth. The radiators in your home warm the air mainly by convection currents. Try holding your hand over a hot radiator. Do you feel the heat being carried upward? In what direction do dust particles move over a hot radiator? Why?

Note about the experiments that follow: Do not be confused by the slight mixing that takes place between the inky layer at the bottom and the clear water above it. This slow mixing has nothing to do with convection: it is due to *diffusion,* or the mixing produced by molecular activity. The molecules in the dye that is present in the ink diffuse or spread upward through the water. Diffusion in liquids is a relatively slow process.

Convection

1. How to get a few drops of ink into a drinking straw.

thumb

Place drinking straw in ink to a depth of almost 1/2 inch. Press thumb against end and remove straw.

blue or black ink

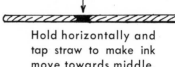

ink

Hold horizontally and tap straw to make ink move towards middle. Wipe ink off end of straw.

2.

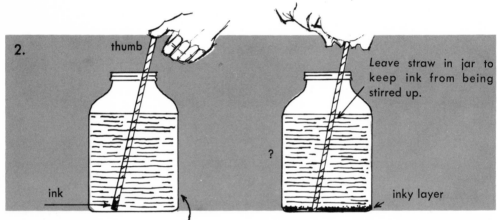

thumb

ink

Leave straw in jar to keep ink from being stirred up.

?

inky layer

jar of cold water from faucet
Insert straw in jar quickly, keeping thumb tightly pressed against end of straw.

Remove thumb and blow through straw gently to force ink out. Wait five minutes. Does ink stay near bottom of jar? Or does the ink mix with the upper liquid quickly? Explain.

3.

Repeat the above experiment, but this time use a jar of hot water. Leave straw in jar as before. Wait five minutes. Does the ink stay at bottom of hot water jar? Or does it move upward and mix quickly? Explain.

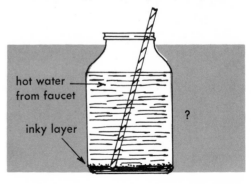

hot water from faucet

inky layer

?

4. Try cooling the bottom layer of the hot water jar.

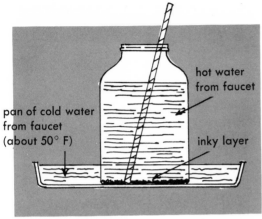

hot water
from faucet

pan of cold water
from faucet
(about 50° F)

inky layer

Prepare jar of hot water with layer of ink at bottom as before. Does *cooling* the inky layer make it spread through the entire jar quickly? Explain.

5. Try warming bottom layer of jar of cold water.

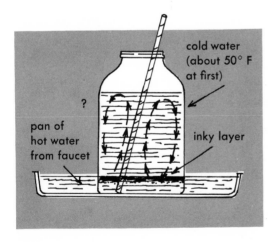

cold water
(about 50° F
at first)

?

pan of
hot water
from faucet

inky layer

Prepare jar of cold water with layer of ink at bottom of it as before. Does warm water in pan cause rapid mixing of the inky layer with upper liquid? Explain. Try putting your finger in top inch of water. Does it feel warm? Why?

5. Also try cooling at top: use jar of hot water with inky layer at bottom. Carefully place three ice cubes in the hot water. Does the ink begin to spread up from bottom? Why?

facts and ideas about . . .

Radiation

You will pour equal quantities of hot water into two small tin cans of similar size. One can will be shiny, the other blackened with soot or with dull black paint. Which can of hot water will cool to room temperature faster? Try it.

You will try the same experiment again, using ice water in the cans this time. Which can of cold water will warm up to room temperature faster — the shiny or the blackened one? Try it.

So far we have investigated the transfer of heat by conduction and convection. In each method, matter — a solid or liquid or gas — was required to bring out the transfer of heat. Now we are concerned with radiation, a method of heat transfer that needs no material medium.

Definition: Radiation is the transfer of energy by electromagnetic waves which travel with the speed of light or about 186,000 miles per second. The energy of the sun is transferred to the earth by radiation. Does this mean that radiant energy can pass through a vacuum? Explain. Hold your hand under a lighted bulb. Is your hand receiving heat by convection, conduction, or radiation? Why?

IMPORTANT FACTS ABOUT RADIATION:

(a) Every body or object, hot or cold, is continually emitting and receiving heat energy by radiation, provided its temperature is above absolute zero ($-273°$ C).

(b) The higher the temperature of a body the faster it radiates heat energy. Therefore the *net* flow is always from a warmer to a cooler body. Can you explain the last statement?

(c) Suppose you place a pot of hot water on your kitchen table. The walls, ceiling, furniture and other objects in the room will radiate heat energy to the hot water; the hot water radiates heat energy to the objects in the room. The water, being at a higher temperature than its surroundings, will emit more radiant energy than it receives. Gradually the temperature of the water will fall to that of the other objects in the room. Why? When that happens the water is receiving radiant energy at exactly the *same rate* as it is emitting it.

The concept that radiation of heat energy never ceases, and that an object at the temperature of its surroundings is emitting and receiving radiant energy at equal rates is known as Prévost's law of heat exchanges. Pierre Prévost (1751–1839), a Swiss philosopher and physicist, enunciated this principle in 1791.

When radiant energy falls on the surface of an object, it may be transmitted, reflected, or absorbed — depending on the nature of the surface of the object. If absorbed, this radiation or radiant energy is changed to heat. A surface covered with soot, which consists of tiny particles of carbon, absorbs about 97% of the radiant energy falling upon it. A polished metal surface, on the other hand, will absorb only about 6% of the radiant energy and reflect the remainder.

To understand the results of your experiments you must keep in mind that good absorbers of heat radiation are also good emitters of heat radiation. And poor absorbers of heat radiation are also poor emitters of heat radiation.

When filled with hot water the tin can with the blackened surface will emit radiant heat faster than it receives it from its surroundings. Why? But this was also true of the shiny can of hot water. Why will the temperature always fall more rapidly in the blackened can? Which surface radiates heat faster — the black or shiny one?

How about the ice-water experiment? Both black and shiny cans receive radiant energy faster than they emit it. Why? Which surface absorbs more? reflects more? Why? Would you expect the water in the blackened can to warm up more quickly than the water in the shiny can? Why?

Radiation

1. Bodies warmer than their surroundings

Are shiny surfaces good emitters of radiation? Are dark surfaces good emitters of radiation?

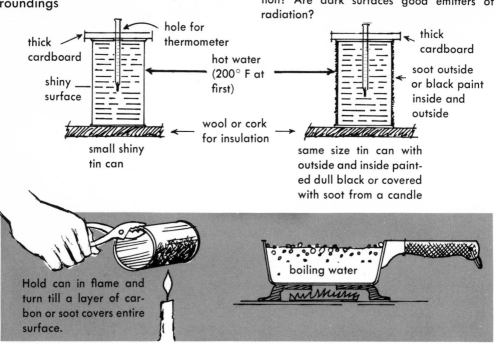

thick cardboard

hole for thermometer

shiny surface

hot water (200° F at first)

wool or cork for insulation

small shiny tin can

thick cardboard

soot outside or black paint inside and outside

same size tin can with outside and inside painted dull black or covered with soot from a candle

Hold can in flame and turn till a layer of carbon or soot covers entire surface.

boiling water

DO THIS: Boil water in pan. Quickly pour this water into the shiny can. Place cover, which has hole through it for the thermometer, in place. Insert thermometer. Temperature will now be below 212° F (100° C). Wait till temperature goes down to 200° F and start recording the temperature of the water in shiny can every minute for 10 minutes and then the temperature at end of 20 minutes. Repeat with blackened can.

shiny can			blackened can		
0 min.	200	° F	0 min.	200	° F
1		° F	1		° F
2		° F	2		° F
3		° F	3		° F
4		° F	4		° F
5		° F	5		° F
6		° F	6		° F
7		° F	7		° F
8		° F	8		° F
9		° F	9		° F
10		° F	10		° F
end of 20 min.		° F	end of 20 min.		° F

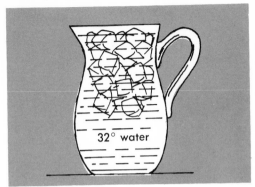

32° water

2. Bodies cooler than their surroundings

Are shiny objects good absorbers of radiation? Are dark objects good absorbers of radiation?

Pitcher or large jar of water with several ice cubes. Stir for a few minutes. When water temperature drops to 32° F (0° C) pour water off into same small cans used previously. *Keep ice out of small cans.*

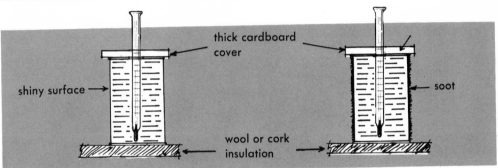

shiny surface →

thick cardboard cover

← soot

← wool or cork insulation

DO THIS: Do one can at a time as before. Pour 32° F water into shiny can. Place cover, with thermometer in it, on can. Wait till temperature rises to 40° F. Then start recording changes each minute for 10 minutes.

Repeat with blackened can, making sure you pour 32° water into it, and *no ice*, as before.

shiny can		blackened can	
0 min.	40 ° F	0 min.	40 ° F
1	° F	1	° F
2	° F	2	° F
3	° F	3	° F
4	° F	4	° F
5	° F	5	° F
6	° F	6	° F
7	° F	7	° F
8	° F	8	° F
9	° F	9	° F
10	° F	10	° F
end of 20 min.	° F	end of 20 min.	° F

facts and ideas about . . .

Infrared Radiation

You are going to investigate the radiation that a body emits before its temperature is high enough to emit light — namely, *infrared radiation*. In the last experiment you learned that all bodies, hot or cold, radiate energy in the form of electromagnetic waves. These waves, when absorbed by matter, produce heating effects. Infrared waves, often called "heat waves," are radiations whose wave lengths are longer than those of visible light but shorter than those of radio waves.

Infrared waves are invisible. The hotter the substance the more infrared waves it emits. The nerves in your skin can only detect the infrared waves emitted by objects whose temperature is much higher than the body temperature.

Infrared rays were discovered by Sir William Herschel (1738–1822), an English astronomer, while he was investigating the spectrum of white light or sunlight. The spectrum is a color band produced when a beam of sunlight passes through a glass prism. The order of colors in the spectrum is violet, blue, green, yellow, orange, red. As Herschel moved his crude thermometer out of the spectrum proper, that is, beyond the visible red, he was surprised to find that the temperature at a certain distance away from the red end was higher than at any other point. The prefix *infra* means below or beneath; infrared means *below* the red end of the spectrum.

IMPORTANT FACTS ABOUT INFRARED RADIATION:

(a) Radiation that produces the sensation of light when it strikes the eye is called visible radiation. These visible electromagnetic waves range in length from about 0.0004 millimeters for violet to about 0.0008 millimeters for red.

(b) Beyond the darkest red are still longer waves, *not* visible to the human eye, called infrared waves. The wave lengths of the infrared range from 0.0008 mm. for the darkest red to about 0.3 centimeters. The longest infrared waves are therefore about 400 times longer than the longest visible waves.

(c) Remember that the wave length is the distance from the crest of one wave to the crest of the next. Also that a millimeter is about the distance between two lines when they are drawn as close together as possible with a ruler and sharp pencil.

(d) Infrared rays, like visible rays, travel in straight lines and are reflected from smooth surfaces according to the same laws.

(e) Keep in mind that a piece of wire, even at room temperature, is continually emitting long infrared waves. This is also true of the furniture in the room, the walls, ceiling, your own body, and so forth. See page 78.

In your experiment you will proceed to heat the wire — but *not* "red-hot." Can you feel the heat when you hold your hand under the wire? The wire, now that its temperature is higher, is emitting more infrared waves because the particles in the wire are vibrating faster or more vigorously. Why? The emitted waves are now a mixture of long infrared waves and shorter infrared waves. But the emitted waves are still invisible. Why?

You will heat the wire again, this time until it assumes a dull red color. Your wire is now emitting long infrared waves, shorter infrared waves, and the first visible or red waves. This occurs at a temperature of about 525° C. As the temperature of the wire is raised still higher, more visible waves are added and the color changes to orange, yellow, and finally white. In other words, between 800° C and 1200° C, *in addition* to the infrared waves, there are so many shorter waves in the visible range that the eye sees the wire as "white-hot."

Infrared Radiation

1. Radiation and temperature

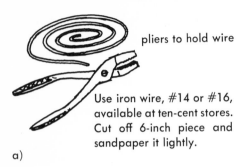

pliers to hold wire

Use iron wire, #14 or #16, available at ten-cent stores. Cut off 6-inch piece and sandpaper it lightly.

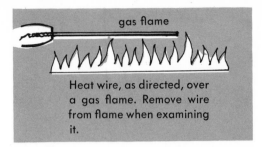

gas flame

Heat wire, as directed, over a gas flame. Remove wire from flame when examining it.

a)

The "cold" wire is at room temperature. The wire is emitting long wave-length infrared radiation at a rate *equal* to that at which it is receiving similar infrared radiation from surrounding objects. (See p. 81)

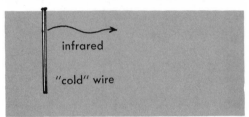

infrared

"cold" wire

b)

The hot wire (*not* glowing) is now emitting more long infrared waves plus some shorter infrared waves. Why? The hot wire is emitting infrared faster than it is receiving infrared from its surroundings. Why?

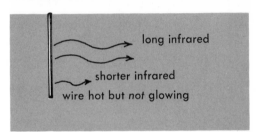

long infrared

shorter infrared

wire hot but *not* glowing

c)

The wire is now emitting long infrared waves, and still shorter *red* waves. These red waves are the first visible waves.

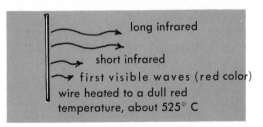

long infrared

short infrared

first visible waves (red color)

wire heated to a dull red temperature, about 525° C

d)

The "white-hot" wire is now emitting long infrared, shorter infrared and still shorter visible waves such as ROYGBV which together make up white light. (The letters stand for the colors in white light.)

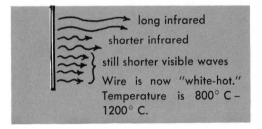

long infrared

shorter infrared

still shorter visible waves

Wire is now "white-hot." Temperature is 800° C – 1200° C.

2. Can infrared waves be reflected?

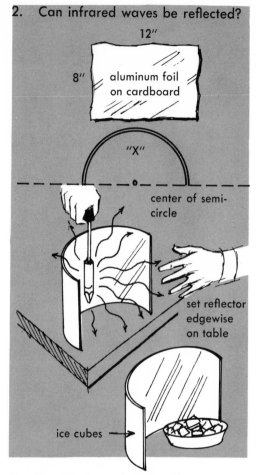

12"

8" aluminum foil on cardboard

"X"

center of semi-circle

set reflector edgewise on table

ice cubes →

a)

Paste a strip of *smooth* aluminum foil on a piece of cardboard. Be sure shiny side of foil is *up*.

Bend your homemade reflector into a semi-circle. When using it as a concave reflector place hot or cold object at or near "X."

b)

Place hot tip of soldering iron at "X." Can you feel the reflected heat or infrared waves on your hand or face? Try a thermometer.

Place a dish of ice cubes at "X," in front of reflector. Is ice receiving more infrared waves than it is emitting? Why? Do you expect to feel the "cold" distinctly? Explain.

3. Try this for radiation of heat or infrared waves from cold objects:

ice cubes

Do you feel the "cold," that is, the infrared waves from the ice or the cold dish? Or is your *face* emitting more infrared waves than it is receiving? Explain.

reflector edgewise on table

Now bring your curved reflector close to the ice cubes. Do you feel any difference in the "cold" emitted by the ice or cold dish? Explain.

facts and ideas about . . .

The Greenhouse Effect

You are going to place in the sun two boxes, each containing a thin layer of soil. One, representing a glass-walled greenhouse, will be covered with a sheet of window glass. The other will be left open. Each box will contain a thermometer. After fifteen minutes in the direct sunlight, you will check the temperature in each box. In which box will the temperature be higher? Why? Try it.

The sun's radiation comes to us from an envelope around the sun called the *photosphere,* which is at a temperature of about 6000° C. At this temperature the radiation from a white-hot body consists largely of electromagnetic waves in the visible range (see page 81). The sun's radiation consists of about 80% visible light, 16% infrared waves and about 4% ultraviolet waves. *Ultraviolet* is the name applied to the invisible radiation of shorter wave length than violet light. *Ultra* means beyond — i.e., beyond the violet of the spectrum (see page 80).

Some of the sun's radiation is absorbed by the atmosphere. But most of it passes through and reaches the surface of the earth where it is absorbed and changed to heat. The earth then re-radiates this heat energy outward, but by waves of much greater wave lengths. Why? Because, compared to the sun, the earth — even when warm — is at a low temperature. The re-radiated waves from the earth are therefore the longer infrared waves. These longer infrared waves cannot pass upward through the atmosphere. In other words, they are trapped in the lower layer of the atmosphere. Do you see why the air temperature is greater at sea level than at higher altitudes?

IMPORTANT FACTS ABOUT THE GREENHOUSE EXPERIMENT:

(a) Glass is fairly transparent to the short visible waves that make up most of the radiation from the sun. However, it is opaque to the longer infrared radiation.

(b) This means that the sun's radiation passes through the glass roof of a green-house with little loss. The short waves in sunlight are absorbed by the soil and by the walls and tables of the greenhouse and changed to heat. As soon as these materials become warm they immediately re-radiate the added heat; that is, they emit long infrared waves. Why?

(c) Glass, as noted above, is quite opaque to the long infrared waves reaching it from *within* the greenhouse. The long infrared waves are therefore trapped inside and the temperature of the air within the greenhouse soon rises well above its surroundings. On a sunny winter day when the out-of-doors temperature is below freezing, the air in a greenhouse may be 60°–70° F. Do you see why?

You will compare the temperature reading of a thermometer exposed directly to sunlight with one that is behind glass. Is there any noticeable difference? Explain.

Finally you will try a similar experiment with the infrared rays emitted by an electric iron. Does your thermometer indicate any absorption or reflection of infrared radiation by glass? Does your hand feel any difference in temperature when the sheet of glass is interposed between it and the sunlight? Do you think glass is fairly opaque to the longer infrared waves? Explain.

The Greenhouse Effect

1.

[Do this experiment on a clear day, out-of-doors, while the sun is high in the sky. Your figures will be different from the ones given here. It depends on the temperature of the air, the season, the dimensions of the box, etc.]

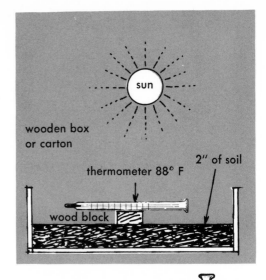

wooden box or carton

thermometer 88° F

2" of soil

wood block

DO THIS: Expose box to sunlight, as shown, for 15 minutes. Then read thermometer temperature in box.

Air temperature in shade was 75° C.

2. The glass-roofed greenhouse as a "heat-trap"

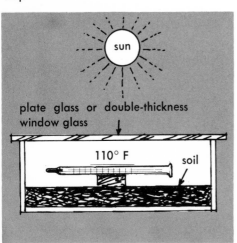

plate glass or double-thickness window glass

110° F

soil

Now cover your box or model of a greenhouse with a sheet of glass. Wait 15 minutes before reading the thermometer.

Why did the temperature of the air in the box rise 22 degrees in 15 minutes?

Why didn't the heat escape through the glass in the same manner as it entered the glass?

3. Experiments explaining the "heat trap" or greenhouse effect.

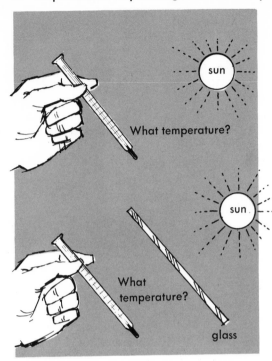

Glass is fairly transparent to the short-wave radiation from the sun.

Hold thermometer up to the sunlight. Do you *feel* the sun's heat on your hand? Read the thermometer.

Now place a piece of plate glass or double-thickness window glass between the thermometer and the sun. Does your hand detect any difference? Does your thermometer read practically the same temperature as before? Does the glass absorb much of the sun's radiation? Touch the glass. Explain.

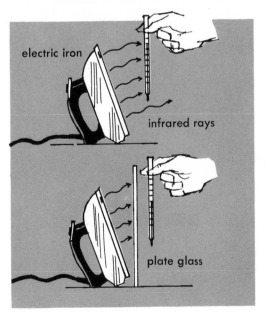

4. Glass is fairly opaque to the invisible, long-wave radiation called infrared or heat waves.

Hold thermometer about 6 inches from hot iron. Do you feel the invisible infrared rays? Read the thermometer.

Keep distances the same as above, but place plate glass between hot iron and thermometer. Does your hand feel cooler now? Read the thermometer after waiting 3 minutes. Does glass stop most of the long infrared waves? Why do we say it is *opaque* to infrared rays?

Further Reading

If you found certain subjects or topics in this book of particular interest, why not go on to learn more about them? In other words, you can make a learning project out of your special interest. Use encyclopedias and textbooks for additional information and a deeper understanding. Wide reading will often turn up descriptions and diagrams of simple experiments you can try at home.

Get into the habit of using the index volume of an encyclopedia as well as the index pages of textbooks. Frequently a subject will be listed under a heading different from the one you may have in mind.

If the presentation in an encyclopedia is too detailed or difficult for you to understand, look for a simpler explanation in another encyclopedia — and then go back to the more difficult one. Follow a similar procedure with textbooks: read a simplified explanation first, and then go on to one that is more advanced. Use more than one textbook; study the treatment of the same subject by different authors. Remember that if a book or explanation seems simple, you are probably ready for one that is more thorough, more challenging.

Standard Encyclopedias

Encyclopaedia Britannica, 1959.
Collier's Encyclopedia, 1962.
The Encyclopedia Americana, 1959.
Compton's Pictured Encyclopedia and Fact Index, 1962.
Van Nostrand's Scientific Encyclopedia, 1958.

There are many good textbooks in physics on the shelves of school and public libraries. If you cannot find the books listed below, almost any recent physics texts will probably be as useful.

Bachman, C. H., *Physics,* Wiley, 1955.
Baker, D. L., Brownlee, R. B., Fuller, R. W., *Elements of Physics,* Allyn and Bacon, 1955.
Blackwood, O. H., Herron, W. B., Kelly, W. C., *Physics,* Ginn, 1958.
Brinkerhoff, R. F., et al., *Exploring Physics,* Harcourt, Brace, 1959.
Dull, C. E., Metcalfe, H. C., Williams, J. E., *Modern Physics,* Holt, Rhinehart and Winston, 1960.
Efron, Alexander, *Basic Physics,* Rider, 1958.
Elliott, L. P., Wilcox, W. F., *Physics,* Macmillan, 1957.
Hausmann, E., Slack E. F., *Physics,* Van Nostrand, 1957.
Knauss, H. P., *Discovering Physics,* Addison-Wesley, 1951.

Physics, Physical Science Study Committee, Heath, 1960.

Semat, Henry, *Physics In The Modern World,* Rhinehart, 1949.

Taylor, L. W., *Physics, The Pioneer Science,* Houghton Mifflin, 1941 (an unusual approach to physics, rich in historical background).

White, H. E., *Modern College Physics,* Van Nostrand, 1957.

Glossary

ABSOLUTE HUMIDITY — the weight of water vapor in a unit volume of air.

BIMETALLIC STRIP — two thin, flat strips of different metals securely fastened together so that their unequal expansion rates may be utilized in thermostats or in thermometers.

BOILING POINT — the temperature at which the vapor pressure of a liquid becomes equal to the pressure on the liquid.

CALORIE — the heat required to raise the temperature of 1 gram of water 1° C.

CONDENSATION — the changing of a vapor into its liquid.

CONDUCTION — the transfer of heat through a substance from molecule to molecule.

CONVECTION — the transfer of heat by a moving fluid as the result of unequal heating.

DEW POINT — the temperature at which atmospheric water vapor begins to condense.

DIFFUSION — the intermingling of gases or liquids of different densities as the result of the individual motions of their molecules.

EVAPORATION — the changing of a liquid into a gas or vapor.

EXPANSION COEFFICIENT — a number or constant that expresses the increase of a unit length of a given material for one degree rise in temperature.

FREEZING POINT — the temperature at which a liquid changes to a solid under normal pressure. *See* Melting point.

HEAT — the kinetic energy of molecular motion.

HEAT CAPACITY — the quantity of heat required to raise the temperature of a body by one degree.

HEAT CONDUCTIVITY — a number or factor that expresses the ability of a substance to transmit heat from molecule to molecule, that is, by conduction.

INFRARED — invisible radiation of longer wave length than visible red light.

KINETIC THEORY OF MATTER — the theory that all matter is composed of tiny particles, or molecules, in a state of vigorous vibration.

MELTING POINT — the temperature at which a solid, under normal atmospheric pressure, changes to a liquid. Melting-point temperatures are also the freezing-point or solidifying temperatures.

MOLECULE — the smallest particle of a substance that has the properties of the substance.

RADIATION — the transfer of energy by electromagnetic waves.

REGELATION — the process of melting under pressure and then refreezing as soon as the pressure is relieved.

RELATIVE HUMIDITY — the ratio (usually expressed as per cent) of the weight of water vapor in a given volume of air to the weight of the water vapor necessary for saturation at the same temperature.

SPECIFIC HEAT — the number of calories required to raise the temperature of 1 gram of a substance 1° C.

TEMPERATURE — a number that denotes the degree of hotness or coldness of a body. Temperature is a measure of the average kinetic energy of the molecules of a substance.

THERMOSTAT — an automatic device for regulating temperature.

ULTRAVIOLET — invisible radiation of shorter wave length than visible violet light.

Purchasing A Thermometer

Inexpensive mercury thermometers, such as are used in school laboratory exercises, are sold mainly by firms specializing in laboratory supplies. Below is a list of several laboratory supply companies. Write to the supplier nearest you and ask about the price of an inexpensive mercury thermometer with a range of about −20° F to 220° F. If you decide to order one, do not send cash or stamps: a check or money order is safer. Please read note on page 39 on using two different types of ten-cent-store thermometers for your experiments if you cannot obtain a mercury thermometer.

Central Scientific Co.
1700 Irving Park Road
Chicago 13, Ill.

Edmund Scientific Co.
Barrington, New Jersey

Fisher Scientific Co.
139 Fisher Building
Pittsburgh 19, Pa.

Macalaster Scientific Corp.
243 Broadway
Cambridge 39, Mass.

New York Scientific Supply Co.
28 West 30 Street
New York 1, N.Y.

Welch Scientific Co.
1515 Sedgwick Street
Chicago 10, Ill.

INDEX

INDEX

The Author

Harry Sootin is a New Yorker who has taught general science and physics in the New York City high schools for over twenty-five years. A graduate of the City College of New York, Mr. Sootin began his career as a chemist, and soon switched to teaching. He was a member of the faculty of the High School of Commerce in Manhattan, and then taught at Flushing High School on Long Island. He has always favored the laboratory approach to science teaching, believing that it is most effective in interesting his students in scientific facts and ideas.

In addition to his teaching duties, Mr. Sootin has devoted much of his time to writing. He is the author of some eight books for young people, including biographies of Isaac Newton, Michael Faraday, Gregor Mendel and Robert Boyle. Mr. Sootin has written many science articles for magazines as well as for the *Book of Knowledge*.

Harry Sootin is a member of the American Association for the Advancement of Science, the History of Science Society, and the Teachers Guild. He makes his home in Flushing, New York.